The Instrument Pilot's Library
• Volume Six •

Training
to
Proficiency

by
The Editors of *IFR* and *IFR Refresher*

Belvoir Publications, Inc.
Greenwich, Connecticut

ISBN: 1-879620-27-8

Jeppesen charts and excerpts are ©Jeppesen-Sanderson and are reproduced with permission. All charts, approach plates and other diagrams are for illustrative purposes only and are NOT TO BE USED FOR NAVIGATION.

Printed and bound in the United States of America by Quebecor Printing, Fairfield, Pennsylvania.

Contents

Preface

This volume of *The Instrument Pilot's Library* covers a broad range of topics related to training. There is a lot of what you would expect from a training manual, such as cockpit exercises designed to keep your skills sharp and advice on dealing with emergencies.

But that's only part of the issue. There's much more to instrument training than rote learning. Much of it has to do with you, the pilot, and the way you approach flying in the first place. In this book you'll find a great deal of knowledge on what makes pilots tick. There are also methods to improve your judgment and decision-making skills. There's even an award-winning article on how to handle yourself if a stressful situation (emergency) does occur.

The book is divided into four sections. Section One deals with the administrative part of staying current and proficient, including a discussion of the instrument competency check.

Section Two talks about pilots, in particular an area all too often ignored in conventional training guides, pilot judgment and decision making.

Section Three covers IFR emergencies, including partial panel, engine failures and lost communications.

Finally, Section Four contains exercises and articles on common mistakes, scanning, and handling your aircraft better.

As always, with these books our aim is to provide you with information you won't find anywhere else. We're not out to replace any of the standard texts, but rather to complement them, thereby giving you greater insight into instrument flying.

• Section One •

Rules
and
Regs

Staying
FAA-Current

A s much as anything else, this book is about keeping sharp, ready to handle the demands of instrument flight. And, no doubt about it, the FAA's minimum requirements for staying sharp simply aren't adequate. In a way, that's a good thing, because it makes getting the rules out of the way easier; it leaves us with the freedom to go as far beyond the minimum as we see fit to make sure we're up to the task at hand.

Annoying and silly as some of them are (ever wonder just what a radio station license is for?), we must all abide by those rules. This chapter presents an overview of what you need to be legal.

The Currency Paper Chase

It starts before you even solo: You have to know the paperwork that must be on an aircraft before you can go flying. As you progress, you learn the recency of experience requirements. When you get an instrument rating, another series of requirements for equipment checks and currency impose themselves. If you're a little fuzzy about what you have to do and what you have to have to be completely legal, here's a review of the basic requirements.

Aircraft Papers

If you fly rental or non-owned aircraft, make sure the following documents are in place:

- Airworthiness certificate
- Registration certificate

- Radio station license
- Operating limitations
- Weight and balance
- Pilot's operating handbook
- Minimum equipment list

An easy acronym to remember the papers that must always be carried in the aircraft is the word "ARROW," which is an abbreviation for airworthiness certificate, registration, radio station license, operating limitations, and weight and balance data. Even as straightforward as these requirements seem, there are some details that can cause difficulties.

The airworthiness certificate, for example, might or might not be valid, depending on whether the required inspections have been completed. All aircraft are required to have an annual inspection every 12 calendar months, which is slightly different than every year. If, for example, your last annual inspection was conducted on May 1. 1995, you can legally fly the aircraft until May 30, 1996.

Want to save 8.3 percent on the cost of every annual inspection? Just take your airplane into the shop on the last day of the month in which the annual is due and have the inspection signed off in the following month. You get almost 13 months on every "annual" as a result.

If the airplane is used for compensation or hire, it's required to have an inspection every 100 hours, give or take 10 hours for special circumstances. Does this mean you must carry the logbook in the airplane to prove the airworthiness certificate is valid?

Not at all. In fact, it's a good idea *not* to carry them in the aircraft, so that in case of an accident, you have separate records.

The registration is another federal document that tells who owns the aircraft. Like the airworthiness certificate, under normal circumstances it doesn't expire, but there's a catch as with the airworthiness certificate. Several years ago, the FAA randomly circulated triennial activity surveys, on which owners were to supposed to report the activity of their aircraft. Owners who didn't return the surveys, or whose reports were retumed to the FAA by the post office as undeliverable resulted in the aircraft being coded as unregistered.

Even though you have a registration card, which technically doesn't expire, it's possible for your aircraft to be out of registration. The only way to find out is to check with the FAA Aircraft Registration Branch in Oklahoma City. The triennial activity survey was discontinued several years ago, so this is only a problem if you've owned an aircraft for more than five years.

The radio station license comes from the Federal Communications

Commission and is required for the avionics. If you don't have a station license, you can get one instantly by filling out a form available at most FBOs. One half of the form is a temporary license. There's no test for the radio station license, no fee and no purpose.

The "O" in ARROW means operating limitations, *not* owner's manual. For modern production aircraft, the required operating limitations are usually in the form of placards and color-coded markings on the instruments. Normally, you wouldn't need a specific document listing the operating limitations. But if you've replaced the plastic side panels or somehow lost any of the placards, you must replace them. We ran up against this when (to our dismay) an FAA inspector pointed out that the placard, "Intentional Aerobatic Maneuvers Prohibited," had been removed from an airplane we were flying.

The weight and balance data required is the actual set of documents that tell what your airplane weighs. Somewhere in the aircraft or the pilot's operating handbook there needs to be a piece of paper with the exact weight and center of gravity. This information is accurate when an airplane is new, but additions and subtractions of equipment, upholstery, dirt, paint and the two-pound Hershey Bar your daughter left on the hat shelf last summer all change the figures.

If you can't find any weight and balance documents, you'll have to get your airplane weighed and start over. Even if you've got some old data, it can be enlightening to have the airplane weighed during an annual inspection. One of the reasons old airplanes don't perform like new is because airplanes, like people, gain weight over the years. A difference of 20 to 30 pounds isn't unusual.

Medical

Once you've determined the aircraft paperwork is in order, it's time to look in your wallet or purse. These requirements may change soon, but as of this writing, if you have a third class medical, it's valid for 24 calendar months from the date of issue. A second class is good for 12 months and then reverts to a third class medical for the next twelve months. A first class medical is good for six months, then it becomes a second. After 12 months, it becomes a third. Although this might seem basic, why not look at your medical right now? You might be surprised. Every year, one or two pilots come to us for recurrent training only to discover his or her medical certificate has expired.

Day vs Night

Now that the aircraft and pilot paperwork is in order, it's time to review currency requirements. The primary requirement to act as pilot in command of an aircraft canying passengers is, during the preceding 90 days, you've made three takeoffs and landings in the same category, class and type of aircraft. Remember, "type" in this case refers to those aircraft for which a type rating is required. It doesn't matter whether you're current in a Beech Bonanza or a Cessna 150. in either case, you're current for any single-engine land airplane.

If you want to fly at night and carry passengers, you must have three takeoffs and landings at night, all to a full stop (no touch and goes). Takeoffs and landings in a taildragger to meet the currency requirements also require a full stop between each landing.

It's a common misconception to believe that a pilot needs to be both current for day and night. If you log three takeoffs and landings at night, you're also current to fly in the daytime. The operative word here is logs. In order to meet the regulations, the flight must be in the logbook. So if you haven't made an entry in the last year, regardless of how much you fly, you aren't current according to the law.

Flght Review

Every 24 calendar months, you must have a flight review from a certificated flight instructor. There are only two requirements for this review. You must go flying and the flight must be entered in your logbook. Beyond that, it's up to the discretion of the flight instructor. It's no longer known as a Biennial Flight Review, and there are other changes proposed, but the substance of the event hasn't changed.

Every two years you have to go flying with a CFI, and he or she must endorse your logbook; cocktail napkins and the backs of business cards don't count.

There's a twist, though: If you satisfactorily completed one or more phases of an FAA-sponsored pilot proficiency award program within the preceding 24 calendar months, you don't need to complete a flight review (FAR 61.56).

Transponder Checks

There's one more bit of equipment certification that applies to both IFR and VFR pilots. If the airplane has a transponder, it must have been checked and certified within the preceding 24 calendar months. If the transponder has Mode C, at least the static portion of a pitot-static test would also have to be done to certify all the black boxes. If you're going that far you might as well get the whole pitot-static check every 24 months. While the pitot-static check isn't required for VFR flying, it's easy to do during the transponder certification.

Currency Checklist

Aircraft Paperwork

- Airworthiness certificate
- Registration
- Radio license
- Operating limitations
- Weight and balance

Required Inspections

- Annual
- 100-hour inspection (airplanes for hire)
- Transponder certification (every 24 months)
- Mode C check (every 24 months)

Pilot Paperwork

- Pilot certificate
- Current medical certificate

Pilot Recent Experience

- Three takeoffs and landings logged
- Three full stops at night, if flying at night
- Three full stops if flying a taildragger
- Flight review within the last 24 months

To Fly in IMC

- Six hours and six apporaches in six months, *or*
- An Instrument Competency Check within the last six months

Other Requirements

- VOR check logged within 10 days
- Pitot-static check within the last 24 months

VOR Log

In order to use the VORs for navigation, it's necessary to have checked them within the preceding 10 days. The VOR receiver check should be entered in a separate permanent record purpose, as if there isn't enough paper floating around the cockpit.

The most common, but least desirable method of accomplishing this requirement, is to tune both VOR receivers to the same station and center the needles. If the two indicatons are within four degrees of one another, you enter the information in the radio log and all is well. The problem with this is both receivers could be 20 degrees off. You haven't really checked their accuracy, you've only confirmed their similarity. Of course, the chance of both radios going crazy in the same direction and in the same amount is remote. Nevertheless, it's possible if not probable.

A better method is to check them at a ground VOR checkpoint. If you don't know where the ground VOR checkpoint is, ask ground control or look in the *Airport/Facility Directory*. A few airports still have a VOT, which transmits a 360-degree FROM signal and a 180-degree TO signal anywhere on the airport. When using these methods, the receiver must be within four degrees of the advertised radial. There's also the airborne VOR checkpoint, which is the least desirable method due to accuracy.

If you want to review VOR equipment checks. refer to FAR 91.171.

Compass & ADF

Here's a test question. If your VOR indicators must be checked every ten days for instrument flying. how often must the ADF and magnetic compass be checked? Would you believe never? Somewhere down the line, it's assumed that the magnetic compass was swung and a deviation card was written up. But there's no requirement to check this in FAR 91.

Likewise, there's no requirement to check the ADF. Although it isn't a requirement, our recommendation is to check these two whenever you're near the approach end of a runway with an outer compass locator. The bearing to the station should be pretty close to the reciprocal of the final approach course while you're holding short of the runway. If not, something's wrong.

Six, Six & Six

As every instrument pilot should know, you need six hours in actual or simulated instrument conditions and six instrument approaches within the past six calendar months to be pilot in command under IFR or to operate in weather that's less than VFR.

Three of the six hours must be in-flight in the category of aircraft involved. If you haven't met the requirement within the next six months, you must without exception pass an instrument competency check (ICC). Note this: you must pass an ICC, whereas a flight review (formerly known as the biennial flight review) only requires that you undertake the review without a pass or fail decision.

The other three hours, and all of the instrument approaches can be "flown" in an approved flight simulator.

We fervently hope that FAA will address the issue of desktop flight simulators soon. In the past five years quite a few excellent computer programs and interface boxes have become available for far less than the cost of the older desktop simulators. With a suitable personal computer, these programs can do everything necessary to properly simulate instrument flight including plotting, variable weather and equipment failures.

Unfortunately, the government hasn't seen fit to approve any of these programs, despite their obvious value. So if you want to log time using a simulator, you've got to use one of the older mechanical units.

A last word on logging simulator time: A CFII has to sign off on the time, which means you have to hire him or her and legally, they must be there with you while you're "flying." No safety pilots here.

When you fly simulated instruments, you must have a safety pilot aboard who possesses at least a private pilot certificate with category and class ratings appropriate to the aircraft being flown. This means if you're flying a multi-engine airplane, the safety pilot must have a multi-engine rating, but need not be current or even checked-out in the airplane being flown (FAR 91.109).

The safety pilot is a required crew member as specified by FAR 91.109(b)(1), therefore, he or she must have a current medical since all required pilot flight crew members must have in their personal possession an appropriate, current medical certificate (FAR 61.3).

The safety pilot must also sign your logbook. If it has been less than six months since you were current. you can just fly with a safety pilot. If it has been longer than six months, you must get an instrument competency check from a CFII.

Speaking of logs, the only flight time you need to log is the aeronautical training and experience used to meet the requirements for a certificate or rating, or the recent flight experience requirements of the FARs (61.51).

When logging simulated instrument time, you need only record the name of the safety pilot and the place and type of each instrument approach. Remember, just because you file and fly an IFR flight plan, you cannot log instrument time unless you're operating the aircraft solely by reference to instruments. If you're acting as an instrument flight instructor, you may log instrument time in actual instrument weather conditions (FAR 61.51)

Enough, Already

If you have accomplished all these things. you can go flying. Considering the sheer number of requirements, it might be a good idea to have a checklist just to make sure (we've drawn one up on these pages.) Oh yes, don't forget the aircraft checklist, the minimum equipment list and the charts.

The Instrument Competency Check

T he very name of the procedure sounds threatening, as if, by implication, you're not competent to fly through the government's airspace on instruments anymore. It's nonsense, of course. The ICC is really no big deal...in fact, we make a habit of recommending an ICC instead of an instrument BFR to all our students, simply because it takes care of currency requirements, and we don't treat it any differently, anyway.

Even when the regs demand that you take an ICC, you can make it work to great advantage, getting not only the required checkup but some valuable instruction time as well. Here are some guidelines on getting a good Instrument Competency Check, from picking the instructor to making sure the check does what you want it to.

Making The ICC Work For You

Some pilots expect the instrument rating to be an "all weather" rating and believe they can fly in any weather and environment. If you believe this, you're only kidding yourself. We've flown with owners of high-performance turbo-charged aircraft who have little or no experience with icing conditions and high altitude flight. Some of these pilots have never been in an altitude chamber, yet launch up to the higher altitudes.

We were asked by the owner of a Beech King Air to fly with his pilot/flight instructor and give an evaluation. As the flight progressed into the flight levels and deteriorating weather. we questioned the pilot about the weather ahead, rapid decompression procedures, and the physiological aspects of high altitude flight.

The pilot had an ATP certificate and 100 hours in the King Air. He had never received any high altitude instruction and didn't have the required endorsement in his logbook. Not only was he not legal to fly as PIC, but imagine what could have happened had an emergency occurred.

There are two types of currency: the paper currency of six hours and six approaches preaches within six months, then there's real currency that includes actual experience within the six-month period.

The recency-of-experience requirements to be pilot in command in instrument conditions are as impractical as any regulation in the book. For example, a green instrument pilot with a dry ticket who holds heading and altitude under the hood for six hours and then completes six simple approaches on a procedures trainer is considered current for another six months. Legally, he can bust cold fronts and fly ILS approaches to minimums.

At the other extreme, a high-time pilot who has flown 15 hours of hard IFR and made five instrument approaches to minimums in the last 13 months has no choice but to take an instrument competency check which could, under the direction of an over-zealous instrument instructor, rival a full-blown instrument check ride.

Frequent Excuses

What causes pilots to get out of currency? A few of the excuses we've heard over the years are:

- "I use my autopilot all the time."
- "I don't fly hard IFR and only go up and down through the overcast."
- "I don't have the time to take recurrency training; I have my six hours and six approaches and I'm legal."
- "I went to Flight Safety last year."
- "Recurrency training is expensive.
- "The simulator doesn't fly like the airplane."

No matter what the reason, you must take charge of your recurrency training. Your instructor cannot do it for you, only guide you on the path to improved proficiency.

Current or Proficient?

In the real world of instrument flying, being legally current and proficient are two different things. A good pilot stays proficient and critically assesses his present level of instrument competency and balances his skill against the weather. But the good pilot who wants to keep his license also better insure that his logbook meets the FAA's requirements.

The arcane wording of the recency-of-experience regulations can pose problems that would tax a Talmudic scholar. It's sometimes necessary to do extensive logbook research to determine if one is current or not. You can be out of currency the day after a perfectly executed five-hour flight in heavy IFR conditions. And it's also possible to be current for one leg of the trip, but to be illegal for the return leg. Your currency can even expire while holding at the outer marker. If you're trapped on top of a thin and unforecast cloud layer at 0005 local time on the morning your currency expires you might consider flying into the next time zone west where he could legally descend in IFR conditions.

Periodic ICC

Naturally, it's incredibly unlikely that anyone is going to pick nits that small. The whole idea is to keep you safe...but it does illustrate how crazy the rules can be.

The easiest way to circumvent all this nonsense is to get an instrument competency check (ICC) every six months. Aside from the regulatory requirement. the instrument competency check is probably the best method to review your skill and discover the weak points of your instrument airmanship. Being current on paper doesn't cut it when you're in deteriorating weather or the equipment fails and immediate decisions must be made. Judgments, discipline and habit patterns only come from practice and experience. While you can legally stay current using a safety pilot, why not benefit from a good ICC given by a competent instructor acting as a check airman?

In order to make these checks both painless and profitable, you must take charge of the situation. Before you make an appointment, you should know how current you are; you should know your strong points and your weak points; you should know those areas in which you need no practice and where you need work. Furthermore, there should be some things you want to try just to challenge yourself. It's like going to confession. A thorough and honest review is in order.

As a safe instrument pilot, you should not need a test to determine these things. You should know them before you take off for every flight. Therefore, your goal for the ICC should be to learn something more than you already know—to emerge a better pilot than you were before.

Finding the Right Instructor

Probably the most important step in the whole process is the flight instructor you choose for the ICC. Remember, when you call the flight school, the person on the other end of the telephone has no particular interest in matching you with an instructor who is compatible with your goals. If you talk to a non-pilot, he/she will try to fit your name into one of the openings on the schedule. If you talk to an instructor, he/she is probably going to try to adjust your schedule in order to get the pay check.

In either case, it's up to you to take charge of the situation. Ask to speak to the chief pilot. If unavailable, have your call returned or call back later. Explain that you want to improve your level of skill rather than just pass a test. Tell him/her what you want to do on your ICC and how you want to do it. The chief pilot may be sufficiently impressed with your approach and will fly with you. Failing that, the best available instructor will probably be recommended. That's who you want.

The next step is to tell your instructor that you want to take an hour or two of instrument instruction. If, at the end of the period you both agree that your flying is safe, you would like a sign-off for an ICC.

Here is where the pass-fail mentality will surface in the instructor. If the instructor sees flight instruction as one thing and the instrument competency check as another—that is to say if the instructor is adamant about the instrument competency check being a test that you must pass, then you know you've got the wrong person. Find someone who seems compatible to your approach.

Your first ride with the instructor will be like a first date. The two of you will be getting to know each other. But assuming the first ride goes well, from there on out you can suggest some things that will make the instruction more effective. Avoid the temptation to take the ICC with a familiar instructor and make the session into flying the same old approaches over and over again.

Challenge Yourself

Once the instrument competency check is viewed by both pilot and instructor as a learning experience instead of a test, a plethora of opportunities present themselves.

An ICC should represent a challenge and should be practical, not ceremonial or routine. It should not only be an evaluation of your skills, but a learning experience as well. We start with a ground review, since this is where we have the opportunity to test the pilot's knowledge of procedures, planning and organizational skills. A practical approach that usually brings out the weaknesses is to have the pilot plan an IFR cross-country. From this we ask questions about airspace, FARs, charts, with a heavy emphasis on emergency procedures and planning.

The weak area for most pilots is weather interpretation and analysis. This is important since a leading cause of general aviation accidents result from flying into weather either beyond the pilot's abilities or the aircraft's limitations.

Knowledge of aircraft systems and equipment is essential. we find many pilots, for example, haven't the slightest idea of how to interpret their onboard weather radar. If the pilot doesn't know how to use a piece of equipment properly, it might as well not be in the airplane. In fact, that equipment could get the pilot into more trouble.

Emergency operations concerning loss of communications and engine-out procedures for multi-engine aircraft is another essential part of the ground review. With the complexity of today's airspace, a pilot must understand the proper procedures to smoothly transition into the airspace system . One area misunderstood is the difference in IFR operations in controlled vs. uncontrolled airspace.

There are no specific requirements for the ICC. There is no requirement for you to fly flawlessly. In fact, much more is often learned by making mistakes.

Try some things that you might screw up. Once you remove the need to do things exactly right, you can work on the things that you don't do well. Consider trying some no-gyro approaches. Spend an entire session on emergency procedures. Fly several approaches without flaps, or find out how fast you can come down the ILS and still hold things together. Then you'll know what speed you can give the controller on final. Lower the landing gear using the emergency procedure while holding the ILS. Don't worry about doing it right, just get it done and learn.

Don't forget holding patterns. Fly this exercise a few times. After crossing a VOR, track outbound to five DME. On the way outbound, make up a holding pattern out of thin air. Just pick a number for the inbound heading or radial and choose left or right. At five miles DME, turn around and head back to the VOR. Enter the hold after you cross the fix. If you can do this repeatedly while maintaining heading and altitude, and if you can pull your fat out of the fire when you blow it, you'll no longer fear an unpublished hold from ATC. Once you master this exercise at a VOR, try it at an NDB.

A cross-country instrument competency check exercises all of the required skills from flight planning to approaches. On the outbound leg, fly it with everything working right. On the way home, have the instructor shut things off. If you can apply all the regulations pertaining to equipment failure on the way home, you will have no problem when you encounter the real thing.

Completion Standards

The method of conducting an ICC isn't addressed in the FARs, and instead is at the discretion of the check airman. However. the recommended procedures and grading criteria come from the FAA practical test standards. The areas usually found deficient are attitude instrument flying (especially partial panel), situational awareness, cockpit organization, single VOR holding patterns and NDB procedures.

If a multi-engine aircraft is used for the check. a single-engine approach is a must. One of our favorite approaches to really see if a pilot can plan and think ahead is to fly the full approach on their own with a circle-to-land maneuver at the end. We always choose an approach that includes a holding pattern course reversal and, to add to the challenge, we include partial panel and allow only a single radio be used.

Many pilots fall into a false sense of security with ATC radar coverage and lose situational awareness. Always keep track of your position by setting up "fences" with cross-radials to alert you to rising terrain. Next, always think of lost communication procedures. Some pilots say, "I carry a hand-held radio." Will the battery be charged when you need it most and will you be able to hear the hand-held over the engine?

There are pros and cons to training in visual versus instrument conditions. In visual conditions, the instructor has more latitude to check unusual attitude recoveries and missed approaches.

Instrument conditions are a great confidence builder for you, but the instructor cannot let you make as many errors because ATC won't allow it. A negative side to training in IMC is that you may encounter delays in high density areas and may be required to execute a full stop landing rather than a missed approach.

When You Need It Most

Last but not least, schedule your instrument competency checks to the times when they will do the most good. Right now we're not flying an airplane that can do battle with cold fronts and icing, so we don't do much instrument flying in the winter. Most of the airways departing our area have MEAs over 8,000 feet which are almost always above the freezing level.

In the spring and early summer, on the other hand, many of the areas we fly to are blanketed by a marine layer. The weather is relatively benign, but ceilings and visibility are often near minimums. So we get our instrument competency checks in the spring, just before we're liable to need the skills most. If we miss the fall ICC, it really doesn't matter because we're not equipped to handle the winter weather anyway.

You might ask, "If I'm going to take responsibility for the curriculum, why do I need an instructor? Why don't I just use a safety pilot?"

One reason is to simplify the idiotic currency requirements. If you fly with a flight instructor and he signs off an instrument competency check, it's good for six months. If you fly with a safety pilot, on the other hand, you would either have to fly for six hours and make six instrument approaches, or you would be back to the old add-up-the-logbook game where you could fall out of grace two days after your flight with the safety pilot. Considering the cost of two hours of flight instruction compared with six hours of avgas, you're probably money ahead with the CFI.

Of course, the most important reason to take the CFI route is that there is a good chance that he/she will teach you something. Once you get past the checkride thinking, a good instructor can impart a wealth of knowledge on your semi-annual training sessions.

• Section Two •

Developing Judgment

Attitude
Rating Quiz

W e're going to start this section with something different: A quiz. This is not a test of your aeronautical knowledge, or your understanding of the convoluted rules we fly by. Instead, this is a test meant to give you a peek inside your own head.

It's easy to fall into the "right stuff" trap, believing that you're somehow superior to others, and that's what makes you able to fly an airplane on instruments with utter confidence and safety, always making the best and wisest choice.

Nonsense, of course. We're all fallible and capable of error. Our attitudes cloud our judgment on a routine basis. But, knowing how your attitude affects your decision making gives you a leg up on it. Here, we hope to give you that insight.

Attitude Check

What kind of decision maker are you?

We don't mean "good" versus "bad," we mean how do you approach a situation where a decision must be made? What's your attitude towards the circumstances?

A conscientious pilot conducts a mental debriefing after each flight in order to review the decisions made during the flight, and how these decisions might be improved in the future. Have you ever thought about the strategies used for making decisions whenever you fly?

This chapter is a test developed to help evaluate your attributes as a pilot decision maker. It will provide insight to your attitudes about flying, and the discussion which follows the questionnaire shows how these attitudes affect safe flying. Based on actual events, the sole purpose of this questionnaire is to determine your decisional attributes as an instrument pilot.

Answer the questions as honestly as possible. Normally, your first impression is the best answer. Following the questionnaire, you will score and interpret the results.

The instructions are as follows:

1. Make a copy of the questions, the Attitude Profile sheet on page 35, and the scoring sheet on page 34. If you're doing it by hand, note the letters next to each blank on the scoring sheet; they're important.
2. Read each of the five situations and the five choices. Decide which one is the *most likely* reason you might make the choice that is described. Write a numeral 1 in the space provided next to that answer.
3. Continue by placing a 2 by the *next* most probable reason, and so on, until you fill all five blanks with ratings of 1, 2, 3, 4 and 5.
4. Read all 10 situations and fill in each blank, even though you may disagree with the choices listed. There are no correct or best answers. Chances are you won't agree with any of the choices. That's intentional.
5. When you're finished, copy your answers over to the scoring sheet. Each situation should add up to 15 (1+2+3+4+5).
6. Total the columns to get a score for each scale. The sum of the five column scores should be 150.
7. Mark your totals for each scale on the Attitude Profile. This will give you a bar chart. The notes at the end of the chapter will tell you how to interpret your score.

Pencils ready? Here goes:

Situation 1

Near the end of a long flight, the weather at destination is 800 overcast, visibility 1/2 mile, fog and haze. The aircraft ahead of you just declared a missed approach (ILS minimums are 200 and 1/2). You elect to attempt the ILS approach. Why?

_____ a. Ceiling and visibility estimates are frequently inaccurate.
_____ b. You are a better pilot than the one who just missed the approach.
_____ c. You might as well try, you cannot change the weather.
_____ d. Your are tired and just want to land.
_____ e. You have always been able to complete approaches under these circumstances in the past.

Situation 2

You plan an important flight under instrument conditions into an area with forecast "light to moderate rime or mixed icing in clouds, and precipitation above the freezing level." You decide to make the trip in an aircraft with no deicing equipment, thinking:

_____ a. You believe that your cruising altitude can be modified to avoid any ice.

_____ b. You have been in this situation often, and nothing has ever happened.

_____ c. You must attend an important meeting in two hours and cannot wait.

_____ d. You never allow an icing forecast to stop you; weather briefers are usually overly cautious..pa

_____ e. There isn't anything you can do about the weather.

Situation 3

You arrive at the airport with a friend, planning to meet another friend arriving on a commercial flight at your destination. The airplane to be used is grounded for avionics repairs. You are offered another aircraft equipped with unfamiliar avionics. You depart on an instrument flight in that aircraft without an equipment briefing. Why?

_____ a. If the avionics were beyond your ability to operate, the FBO would not have offered the use of the airplane.

_____ b. You are in a hurry to meet the commercial flight.

_____ c. Avionics check-outs are rarely necessary.

_____ d. You do not want to admit your unfamiliarity with the avionics.

_____ e. You probably won't need all the radios anyway.

Situation 4

You arrive at destination to pick up a friend after the fuel pumps have closed. Your calculations before departing determined that there would be fuel sufficient to complete the trip, but without the required reserves. The winds en route were stronger than anticipated, and you are not certain of the exact fuel consumption. You decide to return home without refueling since:

_____ a. You cannot remain overnight. Both you and your passenger must be at the office in the morning.

_____ b. The fuel reserves required by the regulations are conservative.

_____ c. The winds will probably diminish during the return trip.

_____ d. You do not wish to reveal your lack of planning to your passenger.

_____ e. It's not your fault the airport services are not available. You will have to try and make the return flight anyway.

Situation 5

You are cleared for an approach during an instrument practice flight with a friend acting as safety pilot. When crossing the outer marker, the controller informs you of a low-level windshear alert for the intended runway. You continue the approach. Why?

_____ a. You want to demonstrate to your friend that you can complete the approach despite windshear.

_____ b. The approach is perfect thus far; nothing is likely to happen.

_____ c. These alerts are for pilots of lesser experience.

_____ d. You need two more approaches to be current, and want to complete this one.

_____ e. The tower cleared you for the approach; it must be safe.

Situation 6

You are about to depart with some business associates on an IFR flight to Miami, Florida in a multi-engine aircraft. During run-up, you notice a vibration in the left engine. Leaning the mixture does not clear the problem. You depart without further diagnosis of the problem. Why?

_____ a. You need to be in Miami by five o'clock and are already behind schedule. The aircraft can be checked in Miami.

_____ b. You have encountered this vibration before without any difficulty.

_____ c. You do not want the passengers to believe you cannot handle the aircraft.

_____ d. It is overly cautious to believe that both engines must be running perfectly smooth.

_____ e. The aircraft was just released from maintenance. The mechanics would not have released an aircraft that was not airworthy.

Situation 7

While in instrument meteorological conditions, you receive conflicting information from the two VORs. You determine that the two nav receivers are out-of-tolerance and cannot accurately determine your position. You believe that ATC will suggest a correction back to the airway. You are thinking:

_____ a. Try to determine position so ATC won't detect you are lost.

_____ b. Continue navigating on the newer VOR. It should work just fine.

_____ c. You will get out of this jam somehow, as always.

_____ d. Be non-committal if ATC calls. If the controller knew of your predicament, he would only make things worse.

_____ e. Immediately inform ATC that you are lost and demand immediate assistance.

Situation 8

During an instrument approach, the controller requests your fuel remaining. With only minutes to the missed approach point, you wonder about this request concerning fuel status. You are concerned about the thunderstorm activity in the area and assume you may be asked to hold. You believe that:

_____ a. Your fuel status is fine, and want to land as soon as possible before the thunderstorm activity arrives.

_____ b. You are in line with the runway, and believe you can land in spite of any thunderstorm-related winds.

_____ c. You must complete this approach, since the weather won't improve.

_____ d. You won't allow ATC to make you hold in potentially severe weather. The controller isn't flying in this weather.

_____ e. The pilot landing ahead of you completed the approach without difficulty.

Situation 9

You are a new instrument pilot conducting an instrument flight of 25 miles. The turn coordinator does not appear to be functioning properly. The visibility is nearing minimums at destination. You continue the flight thinking:

_____ a. You never really needed the turn coordinator.

_____ b. You recently passed the instrument flight test and believe you can handle the weather.

_____ c. Don't worry; ATC will assist if it gets too bad.

_____ d. You should complete this approach so you won't get stuck here.

_____ e. The turn coordinator isn't needed for such a short flight.

Situation 10

During an instrument flight, you encounter clear air turbulence. You are not using the shoulder harness, and continue not to use it. Why?

_____ a. Using the shoulder harness at this point might give the appearance that you are afraid; you don't want to alarm the passengers.
_____ b. Shoulder harness are not necessary for en route operations.
_____ c. You have not been injured thus far.
_____ d. What's the use of using the shoulder harness; if it's your time to go, it won't help.
_____ e. You need to maintain aircraft control; there isn't any time to fool with a should harness.

Scoring Key

After completing the ten situations, write your numbered responses in the corresponding blanks below for each situation. Be careful when transferring your answers that you place each response in the correct blank.

	SCALE I	SCALE II	SCALE III	SCALE IV	SCALE V	
1	a ___	d ___	e ___	b ___	c ___	15
2	d ___	c ___	b ___	a ___	e ___	15
3	c ___	b ___	e ___	d ___	a ___	15
4	b ___	a ___	c ___	d ___	e ___	15
5	c ___	d ___	b ___	a ___	e ___	15
6	d ___	a ___	b ___	c ___	e ___	15
7	d ___	e ___	c ___	a ___	b ___	15
8	d ___	a ___	e ___	b ___	c ___	15
9	e ___	d ___	a ___	b ___	c ___	15
10	b ___	e ___	c ___	a ___	d ___	15
TOTAL	___	___	___	___	___	150

Your Attitude Profile

You now have a total for each of the five columns labeled Scale I, Scale II, Scale III, etc. Place a mark on the space that corresponds to the total score for each column. Note that the lower numbers are on top. Therefore if you answered "1" to every response on a given scale, your score would be 10 and you'd place a mark at the top of the chart. When you're finished, you'll have a bar chart. Interpretation instructions are on the next page.

SCALE I	SCALE II	SCALE III	SCALE IV	SCALE V
10	10	10	10	10
20	20	20	20	20
30	30	30	30	30
40	40	40	40	40
50	50	50	50	50

The Five Hazardous Attitudes

The questionnaire you just completed is part of a training program developed by the FAA in the late 1980s to improve pilot decision making and, hopefully, reduce the number of "pilot error" accidents.

An FAA study reviewed general aviation accidents to determine if any similarities existed among the personalities of the pilots involved. The study revealed that these pilots displayed attitudes that could be classified into one of five groups; each having distinct characteristics. The "hazardous attitudes" listed below were prevalent in the accidents reviewed by the study. The numeral at the beginning of each attitude corresponds with the scale having the same number on the attitude profile sheet you just completed. The five attitudes are:

I. ANTI-AUTHORITY - "The regulations are for someone else." This attitude is found in pilots who resent any external control over their actions. It is
a tendency to disregard rules and procedures.

II. IMPULSIVITY - "I must act now; there's no time." These pilots who act quickly, usually in the manner that first comes to mind.

III. INVULNERABILITY - "It won't happen to me." This attitude is found in pilots who act as though nothing bad can happen to them.

IV. MACHO - "I'll show you. I can do it." These pilots continually attempt to prove themselves better than others. They tend to be over-confident and attempt difficult tasks for the admiration it gains them.

V. RESIGNATION - "What's the use?" This attitude is displayed by those pilots believing that they have little or no control over their circumstances. They are resigned to let things be as they are. They may deny the reality of the situation, and fail to take charge. They may also allow other people or commitments influence their decision making.

Interpret Your Score

Using the completed attitude profile sheet, connect the "Xs" in each column with a line to establish your profile. The result may be a chart with peaks and valleys, or a line that goes through all points evenly. A straight line through the points across the chart indicates that, for the situations in the questionnaire, you use the five attitudes equally, without any one attitude dominating your decision making.

Any large peaks (ten points or greater) that occur relative to the other columns may indicate a dominant attitude in your decision making. Knowing this attitude may influence your decision making can be a helpful safety check during your next flight. When contemplating a major decision, ask yourself, "Am I allowing this attitude to influence my decision, or am I making the decision that will ensure a safe outcome for this flight?"

Each of the five hazardous attitudes has a positive response which, if followed, can help keep the negative attitude in check.

Listed in the sidebar are the five hazardous attitudes and the appropriate positive responses. Hopefully, this exercise has provided insight to some of your decision-making abilities. You can obtain the complete training manual entitled, *Aeronautical Decision Making for Instrument Pilots*, from the National Technical Information Service, Springfield, Virginia 22161; or, the AOPA Air Safety Foundation, 421 Aviation Way, Frederick, Maryland 21701.

	Hazardous Attitude	**Positive Response**
Anti-Authority:	"Don't tell *me*."	"Follow the rules. They are usually right."
Impulsivity:	"Do something - quickly!"	"Not so fast. Think first."
Invulnerability:	"It won't happen to me."	"It could happen to me."
Macho:	"I can do it."	"Taking chances is foolish."
Resignation:	"What's the use."	"I'm not helpless. I can make a difference."

Factors in Decision Making

Perhaps the most important quality an instrument pilot can posess is good judgment. It's well known that most accidents are attributed to "pilot error" of one sort or another, but in truth many of these can be traced directly back to a bad judgment call on the part of the pilot. Having the proverbial "right stuff" won't help you if you don't have the ability to make the right decision when appropriate.

In this section we'll take a close look at the factors involved in making the right decision, starting with a look at how decision-making affects the outcome of a flight.

Successful Decision Making

An experienced pilot knows that flying requires constant adaptation to change. If you adapt successfully, you arrive safely at your destination. If you don't adapt, you become another story for aviation researchers to ponder. Even if you're only conducting practice approaches from your home airport; weather, other traffic in the landing pattern, radio congestion, fuel and other changes occur during the flight. Each change requires that you make a decision.

No flight is successful if it ends in damage or injury. Success is completing the flight without personal injury or damage to the airplane. Any arrival with you and the airplane unharmed is a success, whether you got to the intended destination as planned, or diverted to another airport due to change. On the other hand, failure is arriving somewhere that the airplane and circumstances pick that results in personal injury and/or damage to the airplane.

There is an important relationship between success and decision making. Accident trends show that the decision-making process does not receive enough attention from pilots when they are flying. The importance of good decision making is revealed by accidents, especially those that occur during instrument flight.

Several studies of general aviation accidents have revealed significant trends regarding decision making. These trends involve:

• Pilot experience
• Pilot age
• Phase of flight
• Type of aircraft
• Accident causes
• Severity of accidents

Pilot Experience

One study reviewed accident rates by class of medical certificate and found that pilots with third class medical certificates have a higher accident rate than those with first or second class medicals. For pilots holding first and second class medicals, the accident rate is higher than third class holders for flight experience between 101 and 5,000 total flight hours.

Recent experience is important for all pilots, since there is a correlation between recent flight time and accidents. First and second class certificate holders who fly less than 50 hours per year have a higher accident rate than third class holders.

Pilots with more than 1,000 total flight hours, but less than 50 hours in the past year, have the highest accident rates. On the other hand, pilots with over 1,000 hours total time and more than 50 hours in the last year have the lowest accident rates.

Surprisingly, pilots with first and second class medicals who have more than 1,000 total hours and fly less than 50 hours per year have a higher accident rate than third class holders with the same total and recent experience. The more highly trained pilots, in this case, have a worse record.

It seems that neither training nor total experience, by themselves, ensure successful flying. Recent flight time, however, seems to be key to a pilot's application of lessons learned during training or previous flight experience.

Pilot Age

Younger pilots show slightly higher accident rates than older pilots, but for third class certificate holders, the rate decreases as age increases and then increases once these pilots pass age 60. The exception to this trend is that of third class holders who have low total flight hours and low currency. In this group, accident rates increase with age.

Seventeen to nineteen year-old pilots with less than 1000 total flight hours, but more than 50 hours annually, have more accidents than other pilots with similar experience. Though age seems to improve the likelihood of successful flying, to a point, current flight experience also influences success in this area.

Phase of Flight

Less than one-quarter of the fatal accidents, with instrument-rated pilots flying single- and twin-engine piston airplanes in IMC, occurred within one mile of an airport (takeoff , approach and landing, etc.).

The picture changes when these instrument-rated pilots fly in VMC, where half of the fatal accidents for this group occurred within one mile of an airport.

Less than 10% of fatal accidents occurred during the visual segment of instrument approaches and during final approach. This indicates that when only basic stick and rudder flying is involved, decision-making problems are reduced below critical levels.

Type of Aircraft

In general aviation, the type of aircraft is often associated with the complexity and type of flight operation. For instance, many pilots prefer using twin-engine aircraft for instrument flight.

Choosing a twin does not guarantee success. Fatal daytime accidents in twins are twenty times more frequent in instrument conditions than in visual conditions.

For single-engine aircraft, flown in instrument conditions by instrument-rated pilots, half of the fatal accidents result from airframe failure and loss of control. The other half of the accidents result from a collision with obstacles or the ground while the pilot was in full control (this was also true for twins).One study examined temperature at the time of the accident as a factor. In the accidents reviewed, when the temperature was above 60°F, instrument-rated pilots had nine times more fatal accidents in instrument conditions than in visual conditions. The rate was the same for single and twins.

When the temperature at the time of the accident was below 49°F, the fatal instrument accident was more than twenty times as frequent as the fatal visual accident.

Turbulence-related airframe failures and loss of control occur more frequently in IMC to single-engine airplanes, but are only 1/5 to 1/10 as common for twins. For the twin, when instrument-rated pilots are flying in either visual or instrument conditions, engine failures result in five times as many fatal accidents as for single-engine aircraft.

Accident Causes

In researching the prevalent causes of pilot-induced accidents, one FAA study isolated ten cause/factors in accidents involving private pilots. The ten are:

1. Continued VFR flight into adverse weather.
2. Failure to maintain flying speed.
3. Insufficient terrain clearance en route.
4. Lost control in adverse weather.
5. Failed to avoid collision with ground/water.
6. Failed to maintain safe altitude.
7. Failed to avoid aircraft with both in flight.
8. Takeoff into adverse weather.
9. Lost ground reference in night VFR.
10. Improper instrument procedure in takeoff/landing.

The first three cause/factors account for 11% of non-fatal accidents and 40% of fatal accidents, with the first being the leading cause of fatal accidents. To further underscore the importance of these three cause/factors, approximately 20% of private pilot accidents are fatal, yet 47% of the accidents for these three cause/factors were fatal.

Five of the cause/factors directly involve weather and the other five are related to weather encounters. Each accident resulting from these, especially the weather related accidents, is the unsuccessful outcome of a pilot's decision making process.

Severity of Accidents

By now, your reading probably has sparked some ideas regarding accident patterns. The cause/factor list above includes few, if any, items that are directly linked to skill at manipulating the controls of an aircraft. In non-fatal accidents, such stick and rudder skills may come into play, but in the fatal accidents, the principal causes involve decision making.

It seems that in visual conditions, when skill at controlling the aircraft is necessary, pilots fly the aircraft well enough that the accident is usually non-fatal. On the other hand, when the pilot is involved in instrument flight and thinking becomes the major flight activity, pilots are far less successful in avoiding a fatal accident. The penalties associated with a more demanding decision making situation are more severe.

Defining Success

Sailing always requires attention and, above all, a clear idea of what can happen and what you're going to do about it if it does.—Timothy Foote

That same idea applies to decision making and flying. We always want to successfully complete a flight by applying decision making skills to what can happen or is happening.

The trends noted above indicate that decision making for pilots is important to success and survival, particularly when flying in instrument conditions. Decision making is a process that is learned and improved with training and experience. Everyone can make judgments, but making a decision can be difficult.

What is a Successful Flight?

Decision making is not a process that occurs once during a flight. It's a continuous process of considering all the minor and major problems that occur either all at once or one after another. Decision making must respond to expected, unexpected and possible situations.

Before discussing the decision-making process, it's important to review the idea of success in flying. Most pilots believe a flight is successful if it accomplishes what they set out to do. A flight from Florence, South Carolina to Pittsburgh, Pennsylvania is considered successful if it ends at Pittsburgh, but not if it ends in Morgantown, West Virginia.

We're all familiar with the saying, "Any landing you can walk away from is a good one." This sounds humorous, but it's not appropriate for success. It implies that as long as the pilot and passengers can leave the airplane unharmed, the flight was safe. Is a damaged airplane and frightened passengers a reasonable outcome for a flight?

A better philosophy is this pilot's description of his career, So far, the number of my landings equals the number of my takeoffs. This philosophy doesn't imply rigid goal achievement. By this standard, a diversion to Morgantown is a success, since the airplane, passengers and pilot are safe.

If the planned outcome of a flight is the only view of success, there isn't room for diversion when the weather deteriorates or fuel gets critical. To enjoy a long aviation career, it's useful to view success an outcome that permits continued safe flying.

Traditional flight training provides the stick and rudder skills necessary to respond to an emergency. Good decision-making skills allow you to foresee problems that may develop. If you improve your awareness of potential problems, you gain an the ability to detect or recognize hazards. The remainder of this article will explain the relationship between risk assessment and decision making.

Four Elements of Risk

When assessing risk, it's important to have a systematic way of looking for it. The most effective way is to consider four distinct areas of flight. These areas are the four elements of risk in flying:

- The Aircraft
- The Environment
- The Pilot
- Time

Each risk element applies to the flight itself and to the mission or reason for the flight. Some risks, such as unexpected icing, may be encountered during a flight. Other risks are present before the flight leaves the ground, such as the need to fly home on a Sunday night in order to be at work the next morning.

To further illustrate flight vs. mission risks, consider the difference between losing your DME en route and flying at low level between mountain ridges to observe potential work sites. The loss of DME is a minor inconvenience, while the low-level operations is fraught with hazards.

Regardless of whether risk is high or low, it's always present since nothing is either perfectly predictable or reliable. The purpose of risk assessment is to manage the major and minor risks associated with flying. Remember, risk is always present to some degree and decision making a constant effort to neutralize risk.

Decision Making Process

The decision-making process begins by detecting potential hazard. Your mind has to be open to what can happen and what is happening. Next, you need to review the four risk elements and then act to reduce or eliminate increasing risk in any of the four elements. Think of this as weighing or balancing the risk elements. You should be able to continually counteract the total risk of all four elements.

Total risk can change suddenly. An inoperative ILS receiver may be a minor risk if there is a second one on board, but an inoperative alternator is not. The two, taken together, add up to a greater total risk.

If risk increases in one of the four elements, likelihood of success is diminished unless you take action to neutralize the risk, e.g., use a different radio, divert to an alternate, etc. If you want to counteract or neutralize your risk, you must weigh the risks before taking action.

To do this you need to organize your thinking to consider how much risk lies in each of the four risk elements. Aircraft equipment may be inoperative or not installed, the weather may deteriorate below forecast conditions, you may be flying with a severe cold or a background of intense family or business related stress, and time may be critical due to a lack of fuel. To weigh risk, think of each element a scale. Based on training and experience, review each element separately, and rate its condition. For simplicity, we recommend using a scale of five. Make 1 the lowest risk and 5 the highest risk.

If the aircraft is in good operating condition, it rates a risk estimate of 1. In visual conditions, an inoperative VOR receiver might rate a risk of 2, however, you would change that to a 3 or 4 if you're in IMC.

Risk assessment should be a continuous process since circumstances constantly change. You might decide that the estimate of risk for the aircraft, the environment or the pilot is zero, but this can't work for time. Time always passes, so there's always some stress due to time.

Evaluating Risk

Controlling risk requires a decision to counteract it. For example, to counteract a low fuel condition, you must decide to land and refuel. If you're under intense pressure at work, you can have someone else fly or decide not fly at all. You must actively review risk and make decisions that neutralize or control it.

Let's take a look at the four risk elements introduced above: the aircraft, the environment, the pilot and time.

The Aircraft

When you assess the risks associated with an aircraft, you first need to consider whether the aircraft is properly equipped for the flight. Are all radios fully functioning? Does the engine still develop original horse-power? Can you carry enough fuel to complete the flight? Does the autopilot work? Although you probably make this assessment already, you might not think of this as part of the risk assessment process. When making a preflight assessment of the aircraft and the other three elements, if you decide the flight can proceed, then a continuing process of risk assessment should begin. As changes occur, reassess each risk element.

Flying is not like shooting an arrow into the air. An archer plans for his or her shot, then releases the arrow. After that, whatever happens is going to happen without any more help from the archer. In flying, you plan the flight and start a long process of controlling the outcome.

In flight, things change over time even if nothing appears to be happening. For example, fuel burns every instant the engine runs. Realizing that, successful pilots frequently compare the onboard fuel with the fuel required for a safe landing.

The Environment

This risk element is wide-reaching and includes situations outside the aircraft. An environmental risk is one that limits, modifies or affects the other risk elements.

Weather is an obvious example of the environment. A less obvious example is the regulations under which you operate. Pilots must safely and legally fly in the environment of FAR Part 91, 121, 135, etc.

Another example is the airports you may use. If your destination is in mountainous terrain and is served only by a non-precision approach with circling minimums, you may need to reconsider if the weather isn't favorable and you aren't proficient.

The pilot

Pilots are another part of the risk equation. Too much stress can harm an aircraft. That's true for pilots also. Stress affects your ability to conduct a flight and your risk. There are four types of pilot stress:

• Physical Stress - includes environmental factors that affect a pilot's well being, such as temperature, humidity, noise, vibration and lack of oxygen.
• Physiological Stress - pilot physical conditions such as overweight, lack of sleep, improper diet and illness.
• Psychological Stress - includes internal emotional conditions and the need to make decisions while flying.
• Sociological Stress - outside emotional stresses such as marital problems, family illnesses or deaths and job pressures.

Each stressor can raise risk, but you can counteract stress and reduce risk by:

• Learning how to manage stress.
• Making decisions systematically.
• Keeping your flight workload as low as possible.
• Not rushing in an emergency.

- Keeping current in your aircraft.
- Knowing the limits of your skill.
- Not accumulating concern over mistakes.
- Not flying if you don't feel comfortable about the situation.

Training and Proficiency

Instrument pilots prove they have the skill to fly in instrument conditions during the flight check. That skill probably holds for the next several months. But six months to a year later, this skill may not be as sharp enough to neutralize risk in IFR flight.

During preflight, then in flight, you need to ask yourself several questions:

- Have I had recent practice or instruction that makes me able to fly the airplane in the manner that I and my passengers expect?
- Have I had recent practice or instruction that makes me able to fly to the places that I intend to visit?
- Does my proficiency meet the requirements of the weather, condition of the aircraft, and other factors? Despite what you might wish, the answer to these questions may be, No! If that's the case, you need an alternate plan.

Time

Time is slightly different from the other risk elements. To some extent, time risks are brought on by the other three elements, e.g. fuel consumption, pressure to arrive by a certain time, etc. Time also exists on its own as a risk element. It never stops.

As you sit in the cockpit wondering how to cope with a worsening situation, time continues to pass even though you are absorbed in the problem at hand. In one such case, a commercial airliner ran out of fuel and crashed because the captain was preoccupied with solving a landing gear problem. Time ran out.

In dealing with time as a risk element, you need to reduce or eliminate its impact. You can do this by actions such as landing at a closer airport than planned, by not flying until the next day, by postponing the meeting, etc.

By maintaining a sense of time, successful pilots don't lose track of the overall situation and the position of the aircraft. This is known as situational or positional awareness.

As a deadline draws closer, time exerts more stress on you and can increase risk to unmanageable levels. If time is short, or if you perceive it's short, impulsive behavior can result.

Time doesn't just add to the overall risk, it multiplies it. On the other hand, if you're able to neutralize or balance your time problem, you can achieve a quick and drastic reduction in overall risk.

Practical Applications

So far we've talked about successful IFR decision making in a theoretical way, starting with a look at how decision making affects flight outcomes, followed by a an examination of the factors that go into pilot decisions. What about the real world? How do you actually use all of this?

Let's apply some of what we've learned here to a real flight, which sadly ended in a fatal crash. For our illustration, we'll use an accident covered in Volume 5 of the book series, *IFR Accidents*. It's in the chapter called "Reacting Appropriately," starting on page 83 of that book. Here's a summary if you don't have the book handy:

The flight was a training mission in a Cessna 152, out of Ruston, Louisiana. The actual purpose of the flight was to allow the student to do some cross-country work in VFR conditions. Ruston was IFR at the time, however, so the plan was to depart IFR, then cancel once VMC was reached.

The weather is pertinent: There was a cold front in the area, with good weather behind it. Dallas and Shreveport were both VFR, as was El Dorado, Arkansas, 40 miles to the north. The instructor was briefed to proceed to El Dorado if any problems were encountered.

Eight minutes after departure and shortly after leveling at 4,000, the flight instructor told Center that the gyros had failed, requested a descent out of the clouds and a return to Ruston. (The post-crash investigation revealed that only the heading indicator had failed; the AI was functioning normally.)

The decision here was where to go: Dallas was not a good choice, because that would mean penetrating the front. Ruston was closest and a fair choice, though the weather was moving towards it. El Dorado was 40 miles off and an excellent alternate. The instructor evidently fixated on returning to Ruston and descending to VMC.

After a minute or two of confusion during which the Cessna wandered off course, ATC told the pilot that the last couple of aircraft that tried to get into Ruston didn't make VFR, and asked if the pilot could make the VOR DME Alpha approach.

The instructor, apparently fixated on descent, asked to get down to a thousand. ATC was unable to comply due to minimum altitude restrictions. The controller did clear the Cessna to 2,000, but there was no response. The airplane had crashed. Apparently the pilot had continued to descend until visual contact with the ground, but the airplane hit the trees first, in control and at full cruise speed.

What Happened Here?

The dictionary defines decision as: The act of separating or cutting off; a judgment or conclusion reached or given.

This definition makes decision making sound like a very cut and dried situation. There's no mention of situational analysis, weighing risk nor consideration of the desired outcome or objectives; all of which are part of a systematic approach to good aeronautical decision making.

The flight instructor in this case eliminated several options and zeroed in on one that was fatal. Perhaps if this young CFI had a more systematic approach to decision making, the outcome of the emergency might have been successful.

What is Success?

Earlier in this chapter we discussed success in flying and the four elements of risk (pilot, aircraft, environment and time). A successful flight is one that ends safely, whether at the planned destination or elsewhere.

Let's apply our definition of success and the four risk elements to this accident to see how this approach can help your IFR decision making.

In this case, the flight instructor did not attempt to continue to the planned destination, but instead chose to descend as low as possible to get VFR and return to Ruston.

The supervisor of flying had briefed the instructor to divert to El Dorado (40 miles north) if there were problems since the weather there was good VFR.

Maybe the CFI rejected El Dorado because it was not the home field. However, the diversion might have assured good weather, a safe landing and a chance to sort things out.

The Pilot

The 21 year-old instrument flight instructor had 550 total hours, with 313 hours logged in Cessnas. She had 61 hours instrument time, of which 36 were under simulated conditions.

Only one hour of simulated instruments had been flown in the previous 90 days. This in itself could have been significant in the instructor's decision making. She probably wasn't comfortable being in the clouds with a failed heading indicator.

With the added stress of the emergency, she obviously wanted to get to VMC as soon as possible. Stress in this situation can cause tunnel vision. She was determined to descend to the minimum IFR altitude in the hopes of finding VMC, instead of making a VOR approach into Ruston.

The Airplane

Granted, a Cessna 152 might not be the airplane of choice for an extended IFR cross-country, but this one had the basic instruments and radios necessary for instrument flight.

Only the heading indicator failed; the attitude indicator was still available to keep the airplane straight and level.

The Environment

A cold front, with low ceilings and visibilities, was moving toward Ruston. Good weather was behind the front as well as 40 miles north, where a high pressure system and VFR prevailed.

The gyro failure occurred eight minutes after departing Ruston, so the flight instructor may have fixed in her mind that it was still VFR for a return. But the weather was moving in from the west.

A commuter flight estimated the ceiling at 1000 feet and two miles visibility. The controller reported that no one was able to get in VFR as the Cessna returned, but the CFI was still convinced that a descent to VMC was possible.

Other Considerations

The risk element of the environment can include factors other than weather, such as ATC, airports and the cockpit environment. This was a dual flight that departed IFR in order to reach VFR conditions so a student could fly a VFR cross-country.

The student must have been anxious about being in the clouds during an emergency and could have been a hindrance he was to the instructor.

In addition, the instructor might have been uncomfortable with flying IFR from the right seat with an inoperative heading indicator.

Time

The element of time multiplies the overall level of risk because you can't press a hold button and stop to solve the problem. The aircraft continues while you're engrossed in the problem. The time element can be either real or perceived, induced by internal pressure.

Other than the decision to depart through the front to conduct the lesson, time should not have been critical once the emergency occurred.

They departed with full tanks, so there was plenty of time to workout a suitable course of action.

With only a failed heading indicator, the airplane was not in danger of falling out of the sky. No turbulence was reported.

There was plenty of fuel to reach VMC and El Dorado. Traveling this extra 40 miles would have left them with plenty of reserves and relieved some pressure since they would have been in the clear.

There was also plenty of time to fly the approach to Ruston and proceed to the VFR alternate. This was a VOR/DME approach, but the controller was willing to provide any assistance necessary.

Total Risk

The overall level of risk for this flight doesn't appear to tip the scales against the pilots. Weather was low IFR but not severe in terms of turbulence or thunderstorms. It was within the capability of the Cessna 152 and they were headed toward improving conditions. There was a good VFR alternate close by.

We don't know the comfort level of the flight instructor to make this flight. She may have been legal to fly IFR. but did she feel proficient enough to handle it? Maybe she departed with the expectation that they would cruise through IFR conditions en route and not have to worry about shooting an approach.

Have you ever departed IFR feeling shaky about your proficiency. knowing that as long as you head toward better weather you'll be okay? This is when you should play the "what if" game and honestly evaluate your ability to handle an emergency.

Get-Home-Itis

Did a form of get-home-itis occur? The instrument failure occurred only eight minutes after leaving Ruston. There may have been a temptation to return in order to get another airplane (or have this one repaired) and continue the lesson.

In requesting a lower altitude. the instructor should have set a limit on how low she would go in attempting to get VFR.

That limit should have been the MEA (2400 feet) or the controller's minimum vectoring altitude of 2,000 feet. Either altitude assured adequate terrain and obstacle clearance.

If it's ever necessary to descend in a similar situation, consider any minimum altitude the same as an MDA or DH. Make a missed approach if you can't make visual contact and try someplace else.

In this case, if the instructor had tried the VOR/DME approach with the controller's assistance, there was enough fuel to miss the approach and head to VFR conditions.

If you ever get wrapped up in a similar situation, ask yourself, "Will my actions assure a safe outcome for the flight?" If the answer isn't a resounding "yes," try something that will.

Repairing Bad Judgment

*I*n the last chapter we took a rather dry look at pilot decision making. For this chapter we'll change the focus a bit and examine the larger issue of judgment, making use of FAA's DECIDE model. This gives you a specific, step-by-step approach to addressing judgment issues.

Later in the chapter, we'll focus on one of the thorniest issues in pilot judgment, the compulsion to proceed commonly called "get-home-itis."

How to Handle Poor Judgment

Flight instructors and others lecture us about judgment and they should. We read how pilots exercised poor judgment or bad judgment in accident reports. This is understandable when you consider that at least 80 percent of accidents are pilot-related (now used instead of pilot error).

Whether the judgment was based on erroneous information or a lack of understanding, the poor and the bad will always appear in reports where the pilot was the cause, effect or factor leading to the accident. Let's look into judgment and see how we as pilots are involved and what we can do about decisions based on poor judgment.

Elements of Judgment

Our thesaurus indicates that judgment can involve any or all of the following:

- appraisal
- assessment

- calculation
- conclusion
- estimate
- facility
- good sense
- logic
- wisdom

For example, if a pilot loses an engine in a multi-engine airplane and avoids a populated area to make a forced landing, many would say this is good judgment. The pilot made an assessment of the situation, made an appraisal of the likelihood of continuing on one engine, calculated the ability or inability of finding an airport, and concluded it was safer to land in an unpopulated area.

On the other hand, if a pilot overflies a refueling stop and runs out of fuel before locating another airport, the forced landing would without any doubt be considered 100 percent pilot related and the result of poor judgment. Let's review some accidents under IFR/IMC conditions where judgment was the primary cause.

Night ILS

A pilot worked a full day and then flew for more than three hours. He attempted an ILS approach at night without the benefit of ATC services.

- The weather was below minimums with strong gusty winds.
- The pilot lost control during night instrument approach in IMC.
- The crash occurred after the second missed approach and three people died.
- He was blown off-course during the procedure turn and executed a missed approach, then tried a non-standard means of orientation for the second attempt and intercepted the middle marker unexpectedly. He began a rapid descent and a right turn, evidently trying to locate the runway and lost control. The pilot's ability to make non-radar assisted approaches was inadequate.

The judgment issues in this accident:

- Did not follow the standard missed approach procedure.
- Failed to divert to his alternate which had a radar approach control.
- Instrument proficiency was well below levels for safe IMC.
- Attempted night IMC to an airport below minimums without radar assistance after putting in a full day's work.

Non-Precision Approach

The pilot in this accident attempted a VOR/DME approach that required a circle-to-land. The airport was below minimums. There was an airport with an ILS 10 miles away. The pilot descended below minimums and collided with trees four miles north of the approach path. This was an executive/corporate operation with five on board (four fatal, one serious).

The judgment issues in this accident:

• The pilot elected to bust minimums. He might have gotten away with doing this in the past, but this time good judgment dictated diverting to the alternate airport with an ILS just 10 miles away. Attempting an approach with the weather below minimums was poor judgment.

• Get-home-itis was the probable culprit fed by self-induced pressure and/or pressure induced by others. Good judgment dictates that as pilot-in-command you must never take the risk of succumbing to pressure from anyone, anything, at anytime, no exceptions.

Departure Accidents

Quite a few VMC/IFR/IMC accidents have occurred where aircraft have collided with terrain and other objects on departure. These were at airports without operating control towers. Judgment issues:

• If the instrument approach has a takeoff procedure it should be used. It has been flight checked and if used will provide adequate obstruction clearance on departure.

• If there is no published takeoff procedure good judgment requires the pilot to refer to and study the appropriate terrain charts before departure.

Lack of Discipline

The above accident briefs illustrate what some experts call intentional risk-taking. The judgment aspect here did not involve errors or inadvertent mistakes. The accidents were the result of lack of discipline and failure to conform to the rules and procedures laid down to ensure safe and efficient operations.

Until the aviation fraternity is rid of the people who do not fly by the rules 100% of the time, we will continue to see too many tragedies resulting in fatalities and wrecked airplanes. In some instances the rules must be ignored when the PIC determines in his or her judgment safety is the determining factor. The circumstances of the incident will reveal whether the PIC exercised good or bad judgment.

Limited Experience

Not all poor or bad judgment accidents are intentional. We find a large number of accidents caused by pilots whose limited training or currency resulted in something being done that should not have been done, or not doing something that should have been done, i.e. failure to use proper emergency procedures and checklists to stabilize the aircraft in an emergency.

There have been many accidents or incidents where, when confronted with an engine failure, the PIC feathered the wrong engine. Sometimes this was done close to the ground after takeoff where an element of panic entered the scenario. The investigation reports of these accidents/incidents usually don't tell us what corrective action should have been taken other than the PIC made a decision based on bad judgment. Why then did the PIC feather the wrong engine and what can we learn from this incident to lessen recurrence? Was it panic?

The DECIDE Model

According to FAA Advisory Circular 60-22, *Aeronautical Decision Making,* judgment is the mental process of recognizing and analyzing everything about a situation, rationally evaluating alternative actions to respond to the situation and making a timely decision on what to do about it. The advisory circular suggested that a good tool to use in making aeronautical decisions is a device called the DECIDE Model, which is used as follows:

Detect - The decision maker detects the fact that change has occurred.
Estimate - The decision maker estimates the need to counter or react to the change.
Choose - The decision maker chooses a desirable outcome (in terms of success) for the flight.
Identify - The decision maker identifies actions which could successfully control the change.
Do - The decision maker takes the necessary action.
Evaluate - The decision maker evaluates the effect(s) of his/her action countering the change.

We know there are many decisions that must be made where time wouldn't permit running down all the steps of the DECIDE Model as if it were a checklist. However, if we practice it in all or as many decisions as possible, its use can become very natural and could result in better decisions being made for all situations. We eventually, with practice, would find ourselves going through the process rapidly and almost automatically.

Let's use DECIDE in an example where a multi-engine pilot takes off into a 300-foot ceiling and experiences an engine failure shortly after liftoff. This is a situation where prompt action must be taken and it must be the correct response to the problem. One of the most important considerations when confronted with an emergency is to not have any mind-set to try and save the airplane. The airplane can be repaired or replaced, the occupants cannot.

Detect: Not much problem detecting this situation. The airplane will yaw very demonstrably toward the failed engine. Dead foot, dead engine will be the prominent clue.

Estimate: The need to counter or react will be obvious.

Choose: The desirable outcome, as a matter of priority, will be to maintain aircraft control.

Identify: When the failed engine is identified, it must be feathered. The gear and flaps must be retracted. To maintain control, the decision maker must never allow the airspeed to drop below minimum control speed (Vmc) even at the expense of altitude. The pilot must be ready to reduce power on the good engine to maintain control.

When the aircraft is under control, some maneuvering can be attempted to either return to the airport or to look for a suitable place to set down. Whatever maneuvering is attempted, Vmc and aircraft control are the deciding factors how much, if any, can be risked. Preparation for an instrument approach must be taken. Note: This situation is one of the strongest reasons for avionics to be up and running on takeoff for an emergency return to the departure or other suitable airport.

Do: The PIC takes the identified actions. ATC is notified of the problem and intentions.

Evaluate: A determination is made if sufficient action has been taken to counter the situation.

The above emergency could be one of the most difficult facing any multi-engine instrument-rated pilot. Our purpose was to illustrate the need for preparing for emergencies or potential emergencies with a logical thought process and approach before they occur. The DECIDE Model could be used for any eventuality in training for the decisions that must be taken to counter adverse aircraft and other situations.

What to Review

Review your aircraft's pilot operating handbook and set up the DE-CIDE Model and work some problems, so that when the time comes to make decisions, they will be done in an orderly, safe fashion. You could review some accident reports and set up the DECIDE Model as if you were the PIC and were faced with the same situation that led to the accident.

Simulation before the emergency will go a long way toward avoiding the emergency or the accident. Simulation, even though it could be crude and without the trappings of a sophisticated simulator is justified when pilots are transitioning to new, or unfamiliar aircraft.

There have been instances where pilots highly qualified in jet or other complex aircraft have experienced emergencies, some with disastrous results. Investigations of these accidents have revealed apathy and indifference to procedures of the less complex aircraft. Many of these pilots have found to their dismay, trouble can be just around the corner with the little birds too when judgment is exercised without respect and knowledge of the special characteristics of small general aviation aircraft.

The effects of density altitude and weight-and-balance weren't carefully evaluated in many of these mishaps. When a pilot is highly trained in transport category aircraft, the application of judgment which would work with the large aircraft may be applied to the smaller aircraft without result. This is why effort with the DECIDE Model in conjunction with the POH would be money in the bank.

What can we do to guard against or minimize poor/bad judgment?

Your Personal Campaign

We'll probably never eliminate all human errors unless we automate the entire process from tie-down to tie-down. Even then we couldn't be certain that some programming error wouldn't send the airplane to the wrong taxiway (if we ever reached this stage of automation). The human brain will cut out now and then; it always has and it always will. But there are some personal efforts that can and must be taken to lower the frequency of pilots exercising poor judgment. Here are some ideas for your consideration:

• Always use the checklists and if an emergency takes place and you don't have time to deal with the emergency checklist, be sure and run down the checklist as soon as time permits.
• Have regular and frequent study sessions with pilot operating handbooks, equipment operating handbooks, the AIM and the FARs.

This will reinforce your knowledge of the systems and procedures necessary to safely and efficiently operate the aircraft you fly.

• Launch a special effort to study and learn all there is to know about meteorology and National Weather Service products. You don't need to be a forecaster, but in my experience, too many instrument pilots have a meager understanding of what is available, and don't have a good working knowledge of how to plan for the avoidance of adverse weather.

• Read, no, *devour* all you can about accidents from NTSB accident reports. Learn from the misfortunes of others and redirect your habits if you think you could be vulnerable to the same situations that affected others.

• Attend as many safety seminars as you can to gather material about good techniques and procedures both VFR and IFR. We all learn something at these sessions. Many years ago we learned at an Air Force safety meeting to never use flaps when approaching for landing in an aircraft with an accumulation of ice. The drag from the ice far exceeds the lift produced by the flaps. Just last year we read about a small airplane that stalled and crashed on final approach using full flaps with ice-laden control surfaces. Someone didn't get the word and the outcome was tragic.

• Try to find an aircraft-type user group such as the Bonanza or Comanche Societies that publish newsletters with safety tips.

• Do some simulation exercises regularly with the DECIDE Model alone and/or with other pilots flying the same or comparable aircraft. The success of the U.S. Space Program is without doubt due to the simulation done by the crews long before the launches were underway. There is no substitute for maintaining currency and working toward improving your execution of procedures each time you fly.

Spatial Disorientation

We conducted a study of general aviation accidents during a six-year period where spatial disorientation was the primary cause/factor. There were 133 accidents with 678 fatalities. Every accident was pilot-related, e.g., the PIC could have avoided the tragedy by, among other things, exercising good judgment, such as:

• Paying attention to weather forecasts and adverse weather advisories.

• Refusing to be influenced by self-induced and/or pressure induced by others.

• Keeping current in all aspects of instrument operations and proce-

dures, especially partial panel approaches and recovery from unusual attitudes.
• Careful flight planning with respect to density altitude, weight and balance, and fuel.
• Complying with the rules concerning minimums, selecting and using alternate airports.

Training, knowledge, experience, discipline and currency are the pathways to decisions based on good judgment. It's up to us to attack the problem of poor judgment head on.

We'll close out this chapter with an examination of a "disease" we've all felt the effects of at one time or another: Get-Home-Itis.

For the ground-bound, this disease is rarely more than an inconvenience. For pilots, however, its effects are often fatal.

Get-Home-Itis is often a hidden killer. When reading the accident reports, the listed cause might be anything from fuel exhaustion to continued flight into deteriorating weather. The real cause may well have been the pilot's intense, sometimes irrational compulsion to reach the destination, even if it kills him.

Preventing Get-Home-Itis

We've spent a lot of time researching the problem of get-home-itis. Our emphasis during training is to help pilots understand and adhere to priorities directly related to flying airplanes. In an IFR workload crunch, "fly the airplane first" is a well-established rule that reduces life- threatening incidents. We work toward this discipline during training.

Why do we have catastrophes that indicate a lack of discipline in making go/no-go decisions? We believe it's the result of pilots succumbing to or allowing themselves to be unduly and dangerously vulnerable to self-induced pressures as well as pressures from others.

Accident data indicate that pilots of single-engine retractable gear airplanes experience more than double the weather-related accidents of single-engine fixed-gear models. The higher accident rate seems to be due to greater exposure and the fact that pilots of high performance airplanes aren't getting adequate weather or don't take timely action to circumnavigate weather.

Pilots of single-engine fixed-gear aircraft frequently flew in marginal weather with little experience or no instrument rating at all. They failed to make decisions to reverse course or land until well after the weather had deteriorated beyond the pilot's capabilities.

Instrument-rated pilots were involved in 28 percent of weather-related fatal accidents over an eight-year period, where IMC was encountered and no instrument flight plan had been filed. Instrument pilots who allow themselves to get trapped by this situation have reacted to outside pressures hardly aeronautical in nature. These accidents weren't emergency related before encountering IMC. They were pure and simple cases of get-home- itis.

Let's review four situations where get-home-itis or get-there- itis played significant parts.

Not IFR Proficient

After giving the pilot a check out in the airplane, the CFII noted that instrument flight was not recommended until the pilot received more instruction. Soon after the check out, the pilot got a weather briefing for a flight to Sacramento, CA and was told VFR flight wasn't recommended. He got another briefing and filed a VFR flight plan to Palm Springs, CA. During the flight, the pilot called Palm Springs Tower and told controllers that if he could get through the weather, he would continue northwest bound to Sacramento.

A search was initiated when radio and radar contact were lost seven miles west of the airport. Cloud bases were 2700 feet msl. The airplane was found eight months later by hikers 15 miles northwest of Redlands, CA at 6600 feet msl, in an area where the mountains ranged from 10,000-11,000 feet msl.

Scud-running, whether by IFR or by VFR pilots, can be very risky business. You may know the geographic area like the back of your hand, but you cannot always be sure the visibility, clouds and weather conditions will cooperate.

Palm Springs Airport is 462 feet msl and, the day of the accident, the ceiling was approximately 2200 feet agl. This pilot had no business trying to scud run northwest of the airport near 11,000-foot mountains. Two final thoughts about scud running: if the airplane or any of its components fail to cooperate, is it worth the chance? And last but not by any means least, can you be sure somebody else isn't out there doing the same thing nearby?

Too Much to Handle

The airplane crashed into a house during an ILS to Hanscom Field, MA. Shortly after crossing the outer marker, the tower got a low altitude alert from Boston Approach on the flight. This was the third time during the flight where ATC reported a discrepancy between the barometric setting and the encoding altimeter. The accident occurred at the end of an 18-hour workday for the pilot, who had just been ill with the flu.

Every preflight must include an evaluation of the pilot, not just for proficiency, but for personal fitness as well. You wouldn't think of operating an aircraft without a checklist. Never head for the airport without a personal preflight. Use the IMSAFE checklist below for this purpose:

• Illness
• Medication
• Stress
• Alcohol
• Fatigue
• Emotion

No One Rescued

A medevac helicopter was en route to pick up a patient. The pilot got a briefing before flight that included a chance of marginal VFR. At briefing time, the destination weather was VFR. En route, the weather deteriorated rapidly with freezing rain and snow showers. No attempt was made file IFR. The helicopter crashed into hilly, snow-covered terrain.

Rarely is a mission so important that it's worth risking everyone's life. Even when you launch on a flight you think you can make, be prepared for the possibility of stopping en route, diverting or making the proverbial one-eighty when conditions deteriorate. It's a mature pilot that makes a decision resulting in a safe outcome, even if the landing is someplace other than the intended destination.

Other Influences

The following happened to us during a recent trip. We had foreign visitors who had never been to the East Coast. During their stay, they expressed a strong desire to visit Niagara Falls and Canada. We arranged for lodging and a rental car. The four of us organized the trip to allow for as much sightseeing as possible.

During our discussions, no one mentioned the weather might impact our plans. As the departure date drew closer, weather systems were forming. Cold air masses were pushing southward from Canada and the freezing level lowered from 8000 to 4000 feet in the Buffalo, NY area. This weather continued until late into the evening before our proposed departure. Forecasts in the Buffalo area called for ceilings 300-600 feet and visibilities one to two miles. The surface temperatures were running 34-37° F and the tops were 4000-6000 feet with moderate to severe turbulence below 10,000 feet. Current observations confirmed the forecasts.

We experienced typical passenger pressure at this point. Our visitors were looking forward to the trip and made no bones about severe disappointment if the trip couldn't be made. Time constraints prevented the trip from being postponed. Our airplane isn't equipped for flight into known icing.

As is our usual practice, we disregarded any comments from our passengers about the importance of making the trip and concerned ourselves with the safety of the flight. We made one last check of the weather with a National Weather Service aviation forecaster, who seemed confident we would not encounter any severe weather and we could probably top the clouds at 4000-6000 feet. From this latest information and pireps, we elected to depart.

We told our passengers we were going, but there was a slight chance the weather might turn against us. And if that happened, they should be aware we might have to turn back or land someplace else and wait for conditions to improve. As it turned out, we were able to remain on top at 7000 feet with only light chop. Descending into Buffalo for an ILS approach we encountered some unforecast light rime ice, which didn't accumulate to any alarming degree.

Listen for the Signs

Get-home-itis and get-there-itis are the same except for the destinations. Listen to the warning signs that you're getting set up by outside influences. Here are some examples:

- If you can't get me there, I'll find someone who will.
- But you promised we'd be able to fly there.
- I stand to lose a very big sale if we don't get there by lunchtime.
- These Super Bowl tickets are very expensive and difficult to get.
- We've already paid for the hotel and rental car.
- The patient won't survive unless we get to the hospital now.

These types of statements could lead us to make the following rationalizations and one step closer to becoming a statistic:

- I just passed my instrument comp check.
- ATC radar can take us around the weather.
- No one else is having problems getting there.
- I'm tired, but the autopilot will get us in.

- There's no other way to get there.
- It looks like conditions are improving.

Develop a Discipline

We're sure you can add many examples to these lists. To cope with self-induced pressures and/or pressures induced by others, we need to develop and keep reinforcing a personal discipline to prevent, to the maximum extent possible, these influences from impacting on flight safety. To do this you need a good and current working knowledge of every aspect of instrument flying. The following are some major considerations, which should constantly be in your mind when making decisions to go or not to go.

1. Weather data and analysis; the products that are available and how to use them in decision making.
2. Aircraft limitations:
- Instrument, avionics and altitude capabilities. For example, does your equipment permit entering all terminal areas (720 com, 200 nav and 40 channel glideslope).
- Weight and balance, anti-/de-icing capabilities and fuel consumption.
3. The ATC system. The selection of preferred routes and whether special use airspace will impact your flight.
4. Your personal capabilities:
- IMC experience; have you flown approaches to minimums recently.
- Proficiency - six, six and six might not be sufficient for everyone. I personally prefer for myself at least 10 hours and 10 approaches every six months.
5. Human nature. Don't promise or commit to an action unless you're doubly sure you can pull it off. It's far better to say, "Provided the weather holds, we should be okay." It's also appropriate to remind people that you don't want them to be uncomfortable or placed at risk. You can always try this, It's far better to arrive late in this world than early in the next.

Ignore comments about other pilots who have successfully penetrated severe weather. When you elect not to go, and a response is justified, try this: "I never compromise safety or I don't take chances or place myself or anyone else at risk for anything or anyone."

Every pilot must acquire and maintain a mind-set that never permits anything to compromise safety and good operating practices. Some pilots consider the airplane just a faster means of transportation and become complacent about its reliability. Instrument flying in particular requires a great deal of proficiency and concentration to ensure we're safe.

Never be too proud to change a routing for better weather, make a missed approach, go around, cancel or postpone a flight for your own reasons. It isn't only your prerogative, it's your responsibility under the FARs.

Stress
and the Pilot

T*here's a whole field of study that, while not dealing directly with pilot skills or knowledge, nevertheless has a profound impact on our performance in the cockpit. It has to do with psychology and physiology, in particular referring to stress.*

One of the cliches about flying is that it's "99 percent boredom, and one percent sheer terror." Our performance during that one percent can make the difference between an uneventful flight and a full-bore emergency. Handling ourselves at crunch time is something that's not easy to do, but believe it or not, it's actually possible to train yourself to react better in a crisis situation.

Fear and Panic in the Cockpit

It's night, and the weather is truly cruddy. The pilot of the high-performance single is flying through the worst weather he's seen in at least a year, and he's really getting kicked around. He's well aware that he hasn't had much night IFR lately.

Suddenly the engine sputters, coughs, and dies. The silence is deafening. The pilot can hear his heart pounding, and the sudden rush of adrenalin has turned his stomach into a rock-hard lump. He remembers that he must first keep the airplane right side up, and it's not easy in all that turbulence. He unconsciously grips the yoke tighter. There's no chance of finding a place to land visually. He's in the clouds, and it's black as tar outside.

Then his brain starts yammering at him, trying to bring all of the emergency procedures he's never had to use to the surface. At the same time, a recriminating voice is telling him he should have practiced them, just in case.

He can't remember the right thing to do. He knows that the knowledge is there, but he can't decide what comes next. Was the boost pump supposed to be in the high or low position? Which tank had the most fuel in it? Didn't he pass an airport a few minutes ago? He feels helpless—out of control of the situation. It's like a nightmare with no place to run, and no place to hide.

He's breathing fast, and the combination of adrenalin and hyperventilation is making him queasy and distracting him further. He feels the first tugs of vertigo, and realizes, possibly too late, that in trying to fly the airplane he's fixated on the altimeter. Now he can't decide where to look first to get the airplane back under control.

The Vicious Cycle

This pilot has entered the realm of panic, where he's so tense and scared that he can no longer effectively fly the airplane. Whether or not he could pull himself out of it in time to save the situation is problematical. He's so wound up that he may be unable to calm down before the airplane crashes.

The situation has become a vicious cycle, feeding on itself. The engine failure in the clouds, at night, started the panic in the first place, and he can't get out of the situation until he stops panicking. But the longer he takes to start taking corrective actions, the worse the situation becomes. This merely increases his fear and panic, preventing him from taking any corrective actions. He's locked up—caught in an escalating cycle of fear.

"When you say he's 'locked up,' what you're really saying is he's experiencing cognitive events that excite responses in his body which go along with fear," says Dr. Harvey Wichman, noted aviation psychologist at Claremont-McKenna College of Claremont, California. "This includes things like increased heart rate and rapid breathing."

The physical changes feed back into the brain, adding to the problem. The pilot gets more excited, leading in turn to more physical changes. "It's a kind of undamped feedback loop," said Wichman. "Like an autopilot runaway—it's a spiraling effect."

Normally, control of this process is automatic. If it weren't, people would go into a panic every time they were mildly startled. However, if the event that causes the fear response happens quickly enough, or if it's perceived as being scary enough, it can kick off the panic cycle.

A problem in stopping the cycle of fear, say the experts, is that the pilot may not be aware that he's becoming panicky. One of the characteristics of a fearful reaction is that it's often more apparent to others than it is to the pilot himself.

There are a number of outwardly visible signs that a person is headed up the spiral. Flight examiners and instructors we interviewed pointed to such signs as sweating, pale skin, clipping of words and sentences, increasing pitch of the voice, and increased breathing rate. We spoke to one flight examiner who observed rapid breathing in a student to an extreme degree—the prospective private pilot was breathing heavily, trying to calm down for his checkride. He passed out from hyperventilation sitting on the runway before the first takeoff.

On the other hand, there are some signs of impending panic that are more apparent to the pilot himself than to others, assuming he will make the effort to take notice of them. Increased muscle tension is one, particularly in the shoulders. This also shows up as a very tight grip on the controls.

Another notable sign of growing fear and impending panic is primarily internal, but may progress to being external as well—verbalization. "One of the things that human beings tend to do is verbalize, to make sense of sensory input," says Wichman. Once the pilot starts up the fear spiral, the brain gets messages from the body that are consistent with fear. "The brain begins a process of making self-deprecating remarks." This sends the pilot still further up the spiral toward panic. Wichman noted that this is a curious side effect of the way the mind works.

We conducted an informal survey of several pilots, asking if they ever talk to themselves in the cockpit and, if they do, what do they say. The responses varied considerably, but every one of the pilots answered with a variation on, "You jerk—what did you do that for?"

Dr. Michael Currieri of the Pilot Performance Research & Training Institute also mentioned verbalization, calling it "negative self-talk." "Chastising ourselves when things go wrong is a very powerful influence. It's like talking down to a small child—they begin to believe whatever you tell them," he said, adding that a pilot who tells himself that he's not going to make it has already gone a long way towards actually failing to save the situation.

Mind and Body

"Fear is hard to define," said Currieri. "It's a highly charged word, particularly for pilots." He noted that it's definitely a phenomenon involving both mind and body, however. "There's no clear demarcation—no real separation of mind and body," he said.

For one thing, fear is very subjective—what scares one person may not scare another. For example, an inexperienced passenger may get frightened the first time he or she experiences light turbulence, while an experienced pilot may not even notice it.

Currieri and his colleague, Dr. Eleanor Criswell, have done quantitative research into the effects of stress on the body. They have found that while fear can be caused by many different things, it always produces the same physical responses in a person. This means that a person who has an irrational fear of heights, an inexperienced passenger being afraid of turbulence (fear of the unknown) and a pilot being afraid of flying into bad weather (fear of a known, avoidable danger) are all experiencing more or less the same thing, physically. "If you put sensors on two different individuals, and subject them to two different stressors, you'll get the same kinds of readings from both," Currieri said.

Currieri and Criswell also noted another physical sign that goes with increased stress. The body's extremities—like the hands and feet—drop in temperature. They offer a simple test a pilot can do to help determine whether he is under undue stress. If he touches his fingertips to his cheeks, and they feel cool (without the pilot being cold in general) then chances are he's undergoing a stress reaction and should be extra careful.

Sense of Control

Part of the mental component of the fear cycle is the feeling of loss of control of the situation. How this affects individuals has a lot to do with a personality trait called locus of control.

The locus of control is based on how a person views the workings of his or her life. Someone with an external locus of control tends to feel that he has little control over his own destiny. Events are likely to be ascribed to luck or fate.

A person with an internal locus of control feels that he is directly responsible for anything that happens to him. He is not controlled by events. He controls the events. The typical pilot, the experts say, has a strong internal locus of control—and the older and more experienced the pilot, the more internal it is.

This means, among other things, that being in control of a situation is very important to the average pilot. It also means that he will be all the more upset when control is lost, fueling the fear spiral once it gets started.

"It's as if pilots have tattooed across their foreheads, in invisible ink, the words 'I AM IN CONTROL!'," said Dr. David Jones, aviation psychiatrist and editor of *Aviation, Space and Environmental Medicine.*

Whether or not control is actually there is not as important as the *feeling* of being in control, according to one study. In this study, groups of college students were given a puzzle-solving task. Unknown to the subjects, some of the puzzles were unsolvable. How hard the subjects tried to solve the puzzles was measured and used to judge performance. (The unsolvable puzzles acted as a control for differences in the students' puzzle-solving abilities and intelligence.)

The test was repeated, only with the addition of stress. The stress came in the form of random bursts of very loud (105 dB) noise. Under these conditions, the subjects tended to give up on the puzzles more easily, and they didn't perform the task as well as those under no stress.

A third run was made, only with the addition of a button which, when pressed, would shut off the noise. These subjects were told, "If the noise bothers you, press the button—but we'd rather you didn't." The result: The scores went up, though nobody pressed the button. The conclusion was that the perception of control is important to how well a task is performed.

Another finding was that anxiety (stress) arising out of anticipation had just as much of a detrimental effect on performance as the stressful influence did. For example, in this study some subjects were told that they were going to be subjected to the noise, but they never were. Their scores were as low as those of the group that was bombarded with the noise.

The import of this finding for pilots seems be that they should not spend too much time worrying about possible emergencies. Worrying about it can lead to anxiety that could adversely affect performance during an emergency.

The Broader Picture

There's more to degrading pilot performance than just fear and loss of control, however. Fear is just one facet of a broad and loosely-defined state called arousal.

Arousal refers to the overall psychological and physical state of an individual. It ranges from utter boredom and listlessness on the low end, to blind terror or rage on the high end. There's no real qualitative difference between being stressed-out, being afraid and being locked in the grip of a blind panic—these are just different aspects of arousal. Thus many commonly-used terms like "fear," "stress," "nervousness," "getting pumped-up," and so on, all blend into one another, being different aspects of arousal with some variations. Of course, there are differences to otherwise similar levels of arousal: Fear and anger, for example, are both states of extreme arousal, but there are physical and psychological signs unique to each.

How well a pilot does his job of flying the airplane is directly related to the level and type of arousal he's experiencing. The pilot in the example above got so scared (overaroused) that he could no longer do the things he was trained to do. Psychologists refer to the Yerkes-Dodson law, which says that an individual will be at their best somewhere in between the two extremes of boredom and panic (see the graph below).

What increases an individual's state of arousal is the addition of stressors. These include just about anything in a person's life, good or bad. Stressors include both physical problems and events (like fatigue, improper diet, illness or injury) and mental problems (like time pressure, recent successes or failures, lack of confidence, overconfidence). They also include frightening events (engine failure, for example).

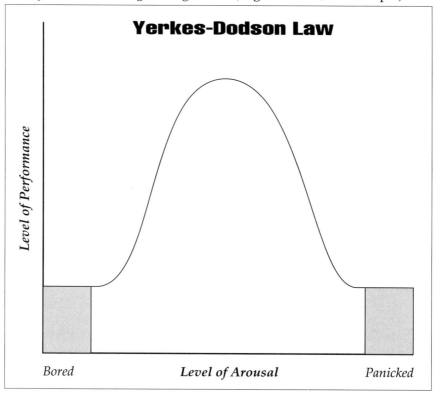

"Arousal" here means the pilot's state of excitement, from utter boredom to sheer terror. This graph shows that an alert, on-guard pilot performs tasks well, and is likely to be on top of any given situation. Too much of anything can be bad, however; go too far and the pilot is "spinning his wheels," getting locked-up and unable to deal with the demands placed on him.

Reserves

How well a pilot copes with an in-flight emergency is strongly affected by the level of tension he brings with him into the cockpit. The graphs on the next page (originally prepared by Transport Canada) illustrate this. The pilot has a certain amount of ability available to perform tasks. The upper limit of that ability at any given moment is defined by a level of stress above which he won't be able to perform well anymore. As shown in the graphs, that level of ability tends to decrease during the course of the flight, due largely to fatigue. The area above the pilot ability curve is the region where the pilot is under too much stress to perform well. The farther above the curve the pilot's stress level goes, the worse his performance gets, until he might not be able to act at all. Psychologists would say that in this region, the pilot is over-aroused.

The tasks a pilot has to perform all make demands on him, and can be viewed as stressors. An emergency occurring while the pilot is performing another task would add to that demand, and may drive his stress level up over the limit line. A given emergency occurring during a high-demand task like takeoff or landing would be more likely to do this than the same emergency occurring during a low-demand task like cruise flight. The area between the demand line and the upper limit line can be viewed as a kind of reserve of ability that the pilot can draw on.

Stress is additive, the psychologists say, so if the pilot climbs into the cockpit already under the gun, all the tasks he has to perform are going to take more out of him than they otherwise would, and place him closer to the upper limit. Chances are he'll be able to get the job done, but it's likely he won't do it very well. And an emergency would be even more incapacitating than it otherwise would.

Dangerous Places

There are particular phases of flight that are critical in that the pilot is under the greatest pressure during them. In an attempt to gather hard information on what phases of flight put pilots under the most stress, studies have been performed in which sensors were attached to pilots and measurements taken during sample flights in both simulators and real airplanes. The results were surprising and unexpected.

For example, most pilots (and researchers) feel that landing is the most demanding task a pilot must perform. But the studies showed that pilots are actually under the most stress at the other end of the flight—during takeoff. One of the first such studies, performed roughly 20 years ago by a pair of Dutch researchers, used a DC-6 simulator. Finding that the pilots in the study exhibited the highest stress during takeoff, they attributed these counterintuitive results to flying in a

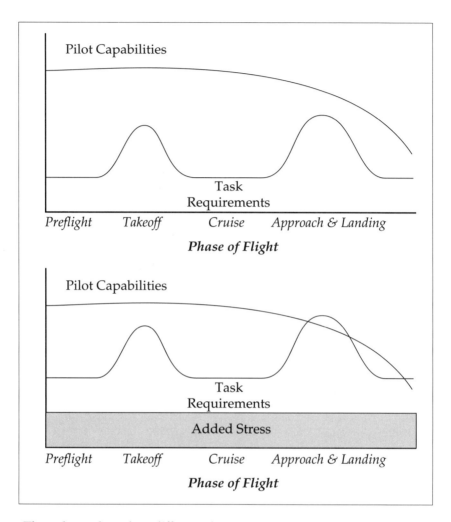

These charts show three different phenomena: First, that the requirements of different phases of flight vary. No surprise here...it's represented by the area under the wavy curve. Second, overall pilot capability decreases with time; in other words, when you're fatigued, as at the end of a long flight, you're less able to deal with demanding situations that when you're fresh and rested. This is represented by the area under the "Pilot Capabilities" line. The area between the task requirements and the pilot capabilities represents a margin of safety. Lastly, if added stress is thrown in, all of the task requirements are bumped up, while pilot capabilities stay the same. This can cause some tasks, such as a demanding approach at the end of a long flight, to exceed the capabilities of the pilot.

simulator instead of a real airplane. Years later, another experiment, which took the same measurements during actual flight, produced the same results.

Emergency Reactions

Jones notes that, "It's not really possible to predict in advance exactly how an individual will react. As good an indicator as any, however, would be how well that person has dealt with stress of this kind in the past. Take people who've been in car wrecks, for instance. If they handled that situation well, they'll probably be alright in the cockpit."

In broad terms, there are three ways in which an individual will react in an emergency, according to psychologists. First, he may react properly and handle it without trouble, particularly if he's well-trained. For example, when the airplane stalls and snaps into a spin, if the pilot is well trained and reacting properly, he'll step on the rudder, put the yoke forward and recover from the spin.

An alternative is that he may panic and take inappropriate action. He might step on the wrong rudder, or try to pick up the low wing or stop the rotation with the ailerons, thereby aggravating the situation.

Lastly, he may freeze and be unable to act, his brain denying that the emergency is actually happening. He'll sit there immobile, hands on the controls, as the plane spins to the ground.

An excellent example of the second category, in which a pilot panics and does the wrong thing, was the crash of a Cessna 421 piloted by famed balloonist Ben Abruzzo on February 11, 1985. Abruzzo's wife and four passengers were aboard.

Abruzzo was attempting to return to Coronado Airport in Albuquerque, New Mexico after the Cessna's nose baggage door came open during takeoff. The door had apparently not been closed properly before departure.

Witnesses said that the door came open just as the airplane rotated during takeoff. The Cessna made an immediate, very steep left turn at a high angle of attack. This put the airplane on a climbing crosswind leg, and it attained an altitude of a few hundred feet. The turn continued to a downwind leg, and abeam the field another turn was made toward the airport. The Cessna then descended into trees and crashed. After impact with the trees, the airplane skidded across an interstate highway near the airport and came to rest upright, bursting into flames. There was evidence that all of the occupants survived the impact. However, they were killed by the fire.

Witnesses under the downwind leg said that they heard the engine noises decrease and looked up to see that the left propeller had stopped turning and the right prop was turning very slowly. The gear was down, and had never been retracted after takeoff.

At the crash site, the left propeller was found in the feathered position and there was no indication that it had been turning at the time of impact. The right propeller was found in the high-rpm position, and strike marks indicated that it was probably turning at about 1,100 rpm at the time of impact. The left propeller control was found in the feathered position and the left throttle was about three-quarters open. The right propeller control was found in the high-rpm position and the right throttle was at idle. Both mixture controls were in the full-rich position. No evidence was found of any pre-crash trouble in either engine.

The NTSB concluded that Abruzzo, unsure of the clearance between the open door and the right propeller, tried to shut down and secure the right engine. He closed the right throttle, but mistakenly feathered the left prop instead. He also failed to raise the gear, which is necessary for single-engine flight in the C-421. Although no one will ever know for sure, Abruzzo's accident bears all the hallmarks of a panicked pilot.

The three broad categories of emergency response are all related to one central process, according to Dr. Clay Foushee, formerly of NASA's Ames Research Center and currently chief scientist for human factors at FAA. "In a crisis situation," he said, "You tend to see the dominant response in an individual. The better-learned a given response is, the greater the probability that it will occur reflexively. There's no substitute for gaining experience [in dealing with real emergencies]—the problem is that an airplane is a bad place to get it."

According to *Aviation, Space and Environmental Medicine's* Jones, physically practicing procedures will help in making them reflexive under stress. "The wise pilot will anticipate the things that can go wrong with himself and the airplane, and develop a plan for dealing with them. Then he'll practice it, either in the air or mentally, on the ground."

Actually going through the motions will give the pilot a kind of kinesthetic memory, he says, in the same way that one learns to shoot a basketball through practice. "The muscles know how to do things that can't be put into words, if they're shown how."

Snap Out of It

Can a pilot recover from panic once things have gone to pot? "Probably not," said one psychologist. "Of course, given time and self-assessment the pilot will certainly be able to calm down." But by its very nature, one of the things an emergency denies a pilot of is time.

One effect of being over-aroused is that thinking narrows markedly—the mind focuses more on being scared and less on anything else the more scared a person becomes. Foushee calls this "cognitive tunnel vision."

"We latch onto one aspect of the situation," he said. "Whatever seems the most pressing at the moment. Parts of the picture on the periphery get blocked out, when the real answer to the problem may lie there."

"The key," says Wichman, "is to break the loop early—to recognize and interrupt the process before the pilot gets overaroused [panicked]." If a pilot begins to feel scared or experiences a tight situation, he should check himself for the most obvious warning signs of impending panic—fast and shallow breathing, tense muscles, and negative internal remarks. The training given by the Pilot Performance Institute goes further, recommending the pilot make periodic "body scans," looking for warning signs, a part of normal cockpit procedure.

Calm Down

"It's important for the pilot to understand that there is something he can do to get himself out of that bad situation," Wichman said. "There are two bits of critical information: First, it's over-arousal that's causing his problem, and second, it is possible to become dis-aroused."

The simplest route to calming down is to alter the way in which the body is acting. Currieri emphasizes the link between mind and body. "If your physical being is out of limits (experiencing a fear reaction), it's going to encroach on your thoughts. There are specific, mechanical things you can do that will have an impact on your body and thought processes."

How does one go about recovering from panic in the shortest possible time? It turns out that there's a lot to the time-honored method of taking a deep breath. Psychologists agree that one of the first things to do to interrupt the fear cycle is to alter the breathing rate. Taking a deep breath and holding it briefly does this and begins to calm down the body. This, in turn, makes the pilot feel more normal and in control of the situation.

But there's a little more to taking a deep breath than inhale-exhale. Specifically, a "deep breath" is one taken from the abdomen, not from the chest. One doctor we spoke with noted that breathing from the abdomen doesn't come naturally for most people, and must be practiced.

Another thing that will help a panicked pilot calm down is reversing the negative "self-talk" that comes naturally when something bad happens. Actively talking to oneself, even out loud, can have a calming effect, say psychologists. The brain hears it, and it will have a positive impact in much the same way that the negative verbalization has a detrimental effect.

Of course, asserting that the situation really isn't dangerous won't work, but saying something positive and definite leading to control of the situation will. For example, some aviation psychologists suggest that a scared pilot might try reciting the procedures he is performing. Not only does this help to calm the pilot down, but it can also serve to refocus his mind on the task at hand.

The object of these exercises is to counter the influences that are driving the pilot up the panic spiral. "To reverse the panic process, you want to emit behavior that's inconsistent with fear and panic," said Wichman.

Also vitally important to reducing fear is getting a sense of control over the situation. The psychologists say that a good way to do this is to attack a big problem by breaking it down into smaller pieces and gaining control of the smaller tasks, one by one.

The sense of gaining control is also related to the self-conmmunication mentioned above. Several pilots we spoke to reacted to tight situations by mentally running through scenarios of what they were going to do next, or what could be wrong with the airplane, and so on. This active thinking about the situation and examining ways out of it lends that sense of control and helps keep the pilot calm, the psychologists say. According to one psychologist, the very act of talking to himself forces a pilot to order his thoughts and start thinking about flying the airplane again, instead of panicking.

Preventive Measures

Knowing how the physical process of going into panic works can help a pilot understand how to get out of it when disaster strikes, but many psychologists advocate going further. Actively learning and practicing stress-reduction techniques, they say, can improve the margin of safety available to the pilot at all times, not just in an emergency situation. "You don't want to wait until you've got an emergency in the sky," said Currieri. "You want to start training yourself now, before you ever get into that situation."

Experts say that by actively practicing stress-reduction techniques before he ever gets into the cockpit, a pilot can do a great deal to keep himself from getting trapped in a panic cycle in the first place. Practicing these techniques can also give a pilot a better chance of catching the warning signs of fear when they do occur.

There are many different stress-reduction techniques, ranging from sophisticated biofeedback systems, to deep concentration, to progressive muscle relaxation. The consensus of opinion is that progressive muscle relaxation is a good place to start with stress reduction, however. Briefly, progressive relaxation involves tensing individual sets of muscles, then consciously relaxing them. The overall effect is to reduce muscle tension. This provides the dual benefit of not only interrupting the overarousal cycle, but also providing feedback to the individual that it's working.

Another place to begin is breathing control, say psychologists. This also interrupts the cycle, and gives the pilot practice in recognizing when he's not breathing regularly.

"You should prepare for the emergency before you ever get in the airplane," said Jones. "You can't practice panic. You've got to look for situations in your everyday life where you get wound up to practice the techniques on, so you can learn to deal with the stress before an emergency happens."

Quick Fix or Full Course?

Will simply knowing about how the fear cycle works and a simple method to break it be enough, or does a pilot need to be trained in and regularly practice stress-reduction techniques to get any benefit?

"On the one hand, just knowing [them] is worthwhile," said Wichman. "Once you get it, the knowledge stays there, but its effectiveness drops rapidly. Pilots who think about it occasionally and use it stay in practice. They're less likely to get into the panic cycle in the first place."

Defining
Your Limits

*A*dmitting to yourself that you can't handle a situation is not easy, particularly for pilots. We tend to be goal-driven, success-oriented individuals. Nevertheless, knowing your own limitations is a key step in developing good IFR judgment. The regs may say that a given approach is safe under such-and-such circumstances, but that's really just a set of arbitrary numbers. The important criteria are the ones you set for yourself—your very own set of personal minimums. This last chapter on developing judgment contains three articles, each covering a different aspect of personal limits.

Personal Minimums

The concept of fixed approach minimums was drummed into our brains during the first hours of instrument instruction. We remember one instructor who was adamant about the fact that if the middle marker was inoperative on an ILS, the minimums increased fifty feet. For Pete's sake! Back then we considered plus or minus 100 feet level flight! What possible difference could fifty feet make?

Next, from our sage instructor we learned a complicated formula for calculating whether we needed an alternate airport and what the forecast weather had to be at our time of arrival in order to file the airport as an alternate. Of course, this was based on the approach minimums at the alternate. After this, we tried to compare the actual reported weather with the regulations and found it couldn't be done. We therefore adopted the simple rule that unless the airport was VFR, and forecast to remain so, we needed an alternate. That was probably our first set of home-made minimums.

Checkride Vs Real World

For the instrument checkride, the applicant is required to descend to the appropriate minimum descent altitude or decision height and then execute the missed approach procedure. Knowledge of the published minimums are important to show you can read the chart and you know when to go from Plan A to Plan B. All well and good for practice and training, but all virtually useless in the real world.

In the real world, assuming the airport is above published approach minimums, the missed approach for an ILS begins when you blow the approach. On a non-precision approach, the missed approach begins when one of three things happen: you get lost on the approach, you get to the missed approach point and you're still in the clouds or you break out and can't find the airport.

In real weather, many pilots can't hold the glideslope and localizer right down to 200 and a half. For those who fly regularly, there are times you can continue the approach to published minimums and there are other times when you lose it while you're still 400 feet in the air. Wind and weather, familiarity with the approach and the aircraft, confidence or anxiety all conspire to make the instrument approach more difficult. Your minimums need to be adjusted for all these variables.

In our case, we've been flying the ILS to Ontario, CA regularly with an indefinite ceiling and a half-mile visibility. Last week the controller asked us to advise him when we cleared of the runway since he couldn't see the first half of the active runway. Under these circumstances, flying our own airplane into a familiar airport with a familiar instrument approach and a weather condition caused by stable marine air, our personal approach minimums are a 200-foot ceiling and one-half mile visibility, the same as the published minimums.

Unfamiliar Circumstances

But what if we were flying a strange airplane, where we had to look a few seconds longer to find what we wanted, and where we weren't exactly sure of the power settings and configuration that would hold the glideslope? What if the weather was caused by a cold front passing instead of stable air? What if the surface winds were gusting across the approach course at 15 to 25 knots? What if the restriction to visibility was caused by rain, instead of fog? What if we had just been through an IRS audit and discovered that the Gestapo was going to take the family farm? All these factors should be added into the personal approach minimums calculation. Remember the discussion of added stress in the last chapter.

The Closer You Get

The odd thing about approach minimums is, the closer you are to them, the better you have to fly, whether you're on the approach or on the missed approach. So if you miss an approach because you couldn't keep all the balls in the air, you still must fly a missed approach to save your bacon.

Flying the missed approach is often more demanding than flying the ILS, where you only need to maintain heading to track the localizer and correct pitch and power to maintain the glideslope. If you blow that, you get to power-up, clean-up and climb on the same localizer you couldn't hold while resetting the radios for the missed approach fix, change to approach or departure control, read and understand the missed approach instructions, all while two quarts of adrenalin are racing through your veins and your blood pressure is approaching the level of the turbocharged manifold pressure.

So the place to employ the personal minimums is before take off or at least before you start the approach. Ask yourself, "Under these circumstances, in this airplane, with this wind and weather, can we track the glideslope to minimums?" If you can't, adjust your personal minimums up to the point where you're sure you can complete the approach. These are the real approach minimums.

The key is a frank assessment of your own skill. Can you fly as good or better than you did on the day of your checkride? How long has it been since you've flown hard IFR? How long has it been since you passed an instrument competency check? Have instrument approaches become easier or more difficult? Add to your personal approach minimums if you find yourself lacking in any of these areas.

More Judgment For Non-Precision

Non-precision approaches require more judgment on your part. An ILS takes you slowly and carefully to a point just off the end of the active runway. Non-precision approaches, on the other hand, often take you via a circuitous route and often leave you at an ill-defined point in space to find the airport for yourself. Although non-precision approach minimums are routinely around 500 feet, the minimums for the pilot and airplane are often much higher.

Circling Complications

If you need to circle to land, this complicates matters further. For example, in many twin-engine airplanes, circling to the right and keeping the airport in sight are virtually impossible. As speed increases, the circling radius increases to the point where it might be impossible to keep the airport in sight regardless of which direction you turn. Many companies that operate turbine aircraft have a policy prohibiting circling approaches for this reason. You should have your own minimums and policy toward circling approaches.

Figuring Your Own Minimums

Here's an example of how you should figure your own personal minimums. While planning a flight to Santa Ynez, CA, (see chart at right) the weather is a ceiling of 1000 feet and one and one-half miles visibility. You review the VOR approach and note that the circling minimums are 1209 feet above the airport. Can you make the approach? It depends. The airport is above published approach minimums, but what about your own approach minimums? Maybe they should be slightly higher.

If you're flying any of the fast twins, like a B-58, Aerostar, or any of the twin Cessnas, you better take a long hard look at this approach. If you can exactly identify Calli (the final approach fix), you must transition from level flight to a steep descent, hopefully without sticking your passengers to the roof. If your groundspeed is 120 knots, you'll be traveling over the ground at two miles a minute. You'll need to lose 1120 feet in a little over two minutes, which means a minimum descent rate of 560 feet per minute, allowing for a few moments to get the rate of descent started.

This descent rate, however, will only get you to the MDA at the missed approach point. If you want to get to the MDA earlier to have time to level off and look for the runway, you'll need a descent rate closer to 1000 fpm.

DME isn't required for this approach, so if you try to identify Calli off the Gaviota Vortac, there's a chance you'll move the intersection closer to the airport because of the acute angle of the intersection. How do you identify the missed approach point if the DME isn't working? Although you could use your GPS for a little illegal "help," without DME the missed approach point is identified by time (which is less precise).But the real killer on this approach is out there 21 miles to the southeast. The San Marcus Vortac, which is the primary approach facility, is over 20 miles away! What does that do to the accuracy of the signal? If your VOR is off by four degrees or more, you'll fly right by the airport and never see it.

In a fast airplane, in actual IFR weather, our personal minimums would be at least 1500 and three to attempt this approach. In other words, it would have to be good VFR before we would file IFR. We

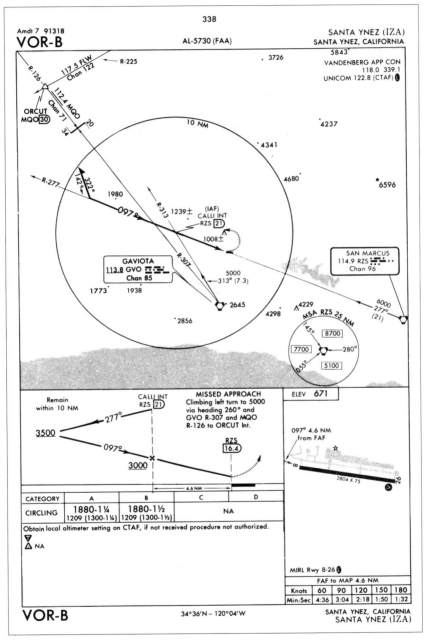

Not for Navigation

would want a ceiling high enough so that we could get under it before getting to the airport and we would want enough visibility underneath to find the airport.

Engine Considerations

As we mentioned earlier, your personal minimums must be set in consideration of your airplane and engine. With turbocharged powerplants costing over $20,000, even the most spend-thrift pilot is making nice shallow descents.

Some airplanes, that were turbocharged as an afterthought, have difficulty making steep descents. The early Turbo Centurions were a good example (or perhaps we should say a bad example). If the pilot left minimum manifold pressure on the engine in order to keep it warm, it was necessary to climb in order to extend the landing gear and flaps. The only way the airplane would track a glideslope below 120 knots was with the gear down and full flaps. If you had to miss the approach, or fly level for a circling approach, a horrendous trim change was required while cleaning up the airplane.

While most airplanes are better than this example, they all have some limitations when it comes to descent. Too low a power setting will wreck an engine. Too many drag devices hung out into the wind could compromise the ability of the airplane to fly level for a circling maneuver. The pilot of a twin certainly wouldn't want to use full flaps and gear on an approach to a circle to land maneuver. If an engine quit in that configuration, the pilot would be one busy hombre trying to stay out of the trees.

So the approach angle must also be figured into your personal minimums. Personally, we look at any non-precision approach that requires a descent rate of more than 500 fpm with a jaundiced eye. If a steep rate of descent is combined with dubious approach configuration, we begin adjusting our personal minimums upward.

Personal Considerations

Once you've accurately assessed your skill and knowledge of the approach, and factored in the performance of your airplane, the last factor you need to put into the minimums equation is your mental and physical health.

Have you been getting plenty of rest lately or are you tired? Are you relaxed, or are you strung pretty tight? Have you had a lot of extra stress in your life—marital problems, legal problems or tax problems? For each yes, you better move your minimums up a couple of hundred feet. These things can affect you so adversely affect that you should consider whether you should fly in instrument conditions at all. In fact, you should seriously consider whether you should be flying an airplane at all, regardless of weather.

VFR for an IFR Approach

A pilot needs to always view approach minimums as just that, minimums. To these figures need to be added all of the previously mentioned factors for you to arrive at valid personal minimums. Be sure to look at other approaches just in case one offers a better deal. Don't be surprised when the weather has to be VFR in order for you to make an instrument approach. It's happened to us more times than we can remember, and we're still here to write about it.

If you're a new instrument pilot, or for that matter just very, very, rusty, you should take care to limit yourself even more carefully than normal. An extra dose of good judgment before flying can make a big difference here.

With this in mind, we offer some guidelines on how to go about defining your limits if you haven't been in the cockpit much recently...or much at all.

Inexperienced? Use Caution

Just about every pilot who aspires to a career as a professional aviator runs into the experience wall sooner or later. That's when you finally get enough certificates and ratings to legally warm a cockpit seat and apply for a job, only to find out you haven't got enough experience; not enough time in the logbook. Come back when you've got 2000 hours, says the would-be employer. "How can I get a job to gain experience when nobody will hire me because I haven't got enough hours?" you ask. It's Catch-22. You go back to flight instructing or hauling checks at night or towing banners until there's enough hours in the book.

There's a parallel to this situation in instrument flying. A newly minted IFR pilot wants to use the operational flexibility made possible by the rating, but doesn't feel comfortable or safe in the airspace system.In the last book in the series, we reviewed an accident that occurred during a pilot's first solo flight in IMC. Only 30 days after getting his rating, he crashed while attempting a night circling approach to a poorly lighted airport, all of this in near-minimum conditions. When we first wrote about this accident in *IFR Refresher,* we received several letters from recently rated instrument pilots asking if we could lay out a plan to gain proficiency that would prevent an accident like this.

This is a delicate area in which to advise, since a host of factors must be considered: the quality and quantity of your training, familiarity with the airplane, the area in which you fly (Outback Municipal as opposed to Chicago O'Hare), the weather and (the most unpredictable factor of all) your willingness to get into real-world IFR operations one step at a time. With this problem in mind, we'll offer some tips on how to get full use of your instrument capabilities at a reasonable pace and with safety considerations given top priority. Our comments are for brand-new or woefully non-current IFR pilots.

Skills and the System

There are two major areas of IFR operations that come into play; your ability to fly the airplane on instruments and your ability to get along efficiently in the system. You've already demonstrated to an examiner you can keep the shiny side up while guiding the airplane through an approach.

But it's unlikely you've progressed to the point where flying the airplane with no outside visual clues is second nature, like breathing. It will get that way if you stay at it long enough, but it takes a while. And until that day arrives, you'll be expending more energy and attention to basic flying than you realize. This leaves few resources to handle management tasks like navigation, communication, positional aware-ness, etc. You need to develop a method to make the flying part of IFR as routine as VFR operations have become.

Most instrument training programs are driven by economics—either yours or the instructors—which means one of the objectives is to get you rated in the shortest possible time. There's nothing wrong with that, as long as you realize when you graduate, you're not ready to face all of the lions in the IFR arena.

Now is the time to hone the skills you learned. There are a number of exercises to serve this purpose: attitude instrument flying practice, constant-airspeed-and-rate climbs and descents, holding patterns, steep turns, etc. These drills will do more for your proficiency in a given amount of time than actual IFR trips or practice approaches. Remember the objective; to get to the point where control manipulation occupies only a small part of your attention.

Sooner or later, you need to get into actual weather and fly actual IFR trips and approaches, which is a lot different than flying under the hood. Here's where location becomes important. Some of you live and fly where the skies are not cloudy all day. As a result, it's prohibitively expensive to fly for a couple of hours to find the right kind of weather for practice. In this case, make sure your view-limiting device truly keeps you from seeing outside. Don't cheat and resolve to keep your personal minimums high until you get some real IMC under your belt.

For those of you who live where less-than-VFR is the norm, look for hazy days when there's no nasty weather around (thunderstorms, icing, low-level turbulence, etc.), when the ceiling is 1000 feet and the visibility is not less than two miles. These conditions let you get used to flying in the clouds by yourself in comfort and safety, since now you don't have an instructor to save the day.

Captain Bob Buck, in his book *Weather Flying*, offers the finest advice ever. He recommends a beginning instrument pilot fly from VFR through VFR to VFR at first, and when that becomes comfortable and routine, fly from VFR through IFR to VFR, then from IFR through IFR to IFR. This might take a long time to accomplish, but it provides a reasonable and safe progression to the point where you can handle just about anything you might encounter (within reason), including ATC.

There's nothing that gets you to the objective as well as the building-block method, in which each individual experience adds something to your total experience. If you go about it one step at a time and don't push, you'll avoid unpleasant experiences that can generate a lot of apprehension and defeat the purpose of this training.

There's absolutely no way to predict how many hours or how many trips or how many approaches make up a satisfactory program of post-rating indoctrination. What suffices for others might be woefully inadequate for you. On the other hand, you might be one of those who can move on in short order. Single-pilot IFR is fraught with potential for disaster until you feel comfortable with the way you're doing things and it won't happen overnight.

Weather Considerations

Weather is a huge factor in a successful IFR-accommodation program. After all, didn't you spend the time and money for an instrument rating so you could fly regardless of the weather? Now wait a minute; that's the absolute worst attitude you could have. There's no such thing as an all-weather pilot any more than there's an all-weather airplane. For every combination of pilot and flying machine, there's a weather condition that simply can't be handled or shouldn't be attempted and the sooner you recognize that the better off you'll be.

For example, you shouldn't get into IMC in an area of known or suspected thunderstorms if you can't see the storms with eyeballs or storm detection equipment. The benefit isn't worth the risk. No one should penetrate ice-laden clouds in an airplane without ice-control equipment. Your next question is probably, "How do I know if there's ice in the clouds?" The answer is you don't know and until you get enough experience to make a reasonably accurate evaluation of the icing conditions, you have no business being a test pilot.

The IFR beginner who is serious about flying in weather that is safe will take every opportunity to experience IMC. That means looking for conditions that require IFR operations and moving gradually into conditions that are more demanding. But at the same time, you must draw the lines of ceiling and visibility in which you feel comfortable.

Again, it would be folly for me to give you a set of numbers to apply to a specific level of experience; everyone's needs and capabilities are different. But we suggest you consider the consequences of setting personal weather limits that are either too high or too low. Too high and you'll never fly IFR, too low and you're walking close to the edge. Especially with single-engine operations, there aren't many options available if The Engine quits in an area of below-minimum visibility. Suppose you break out of the clouds with only a couple hundred feet of ceiling or an eighth mile visibility? You might have to land in the parking lot of the First National Bank.

Multi-engine pilots have more options, but remember it takes much longer to get to an alternate on one engine and your first approach must be right on the money. Engine-out missed approaches are pretty scary and sometimes impossible. Be sure you know the pilot's operating handbook (POH) data for single-engine performance.

When all these considerations are taken into account, consider personal minimums of 1000 feet and two miles to get started. These limits will wipe out a few IFR trips, but they'll also permit a lot of flying in conditions that will let you acquire the experience we've been talking about and do it in safety and comfort. If you're willing to place complete trust in The Engine on a single or on your ability to handle an engine-out situation on a twin, fly an occasional approach to minimums after you feel good in IMC. Problems do arise from time-to-time and it's better to know what a do-or-die approach looks and feels like before you have to do it in an emergency.

ATC Comfort

The second major area of IFR operations for any of us, but especially for beginners, is the ability to get along efficiently in the ATC system. Controllers know they're working with different levels of proficiency and experience when they have both an airliner and a general aviation airplane on the frequency, but they assume both pilots are proficient and knowledgeable and will be able to comply with clearances and instructions. You don't get system smart all at once. It takes time, during which you'll definitely make some mistakes and feel less than completely at ease.

You can shorten your initiation time in this regard in much the same way we suggested for weather experience: one step at a time. Learn from each encounter and put yourself into the system at every opportunity. Even on days when it's CAVU, file IFR. The system works the same, the communication and navigation requirements are the same as when it's zero-zero.

Radio communication is undoubtedly the most nail-biting part of IFR operation for the newly rated. It's something that takes a lot of time to develop. Have faith and, if you listen and learn, it will improve and get more efficient with time. Concentrate on talking clearly and getting your message across with a minimum number of words. Controllers will understand and make adjustments when they detect a tentative note in your transmissions.

And perhaps more important for the beginner than anything else regarding communications, be absolutely certain you understand what you're expected to do. If a clearance or instruction isn't crystal clear, ask the controller to say again. It's not only common sense, it's a regulation. This is especially true in busy terminal areas.

Don't plan your very first IFR adventure to a big city. Things happen so fast you'll probably get behind the airplane early on and it's likely to be unpleasant for everyone the rest of the way. Unless you're never going to fly there, get some experience at a high-density terminal with an experienced CFII in the other seat.

There are ways to get better at communicating without burning fuel. For example, use a portable VHF radio to eavesdrop on both sides of IFR communications. There's a lot to be learned from other pilots, including examples of how not to communicate.

Finally, the matter of whether to use your autopilot has been debated ad nauseum since George came on the scene. If you're convinced that flying for long periods of time straight-and-level will further develop your instrument proficiency, don't ever engage the autopilot. But if you agree there are more important things to be thinking about during cruise, let the autopilot do the flying and apply your talents to managing all the things for which you're responsible.

When it comes to instrument approaches, there isn't a pilot around who can do a better job than a good autopilot. When you're by yourself (that is, the only instrument pilot up front), let the autopilot fly so that you can monitor your progress and look for the runway at the appropriate time.

We're not suggesting you rely on the machinery all the time. Alternately fly both kinds of approaches often enough to maintain your hands-on proficiency. You'll learn more and sharpen your skills faster by flying a variety of manual approaches early in your IFR experience, but use the autopilot when it makes sense. Never let your proficiency drop to the point where you can't take over and do a good job.

It doesn't matter how well you were trained, getting comfortable in the IFR system takes time. The FAA has set reasonable minimum standards for the rating, but those standards truly provide nothing more than a license to learn.

As we noted at the beginning of the book, FAA's minimum proficiency requirements just aren't realistic. It takes more than "six and six in six" to be safe in real-deal IMC. The question is, how much more?

It's another one of those issues which has no cut-and-dried answer. It all depends on you...and that's where your set of personal limits comes in.

The Instrument Competency Line

We're all familiar with the minimum requirements to legally maintain instrument currency. It's six hours of instrument time (half of which can be done in an approved training device) and six approaches in six months. Are you really safe to fly to full ILS minimums if you've only flown the minimum to be legal? How does currency relate to instrument competency?

Tending to Details

There's nothing easy about instrument flying. From the time you start planning a flight until you put the bird back in the hangar at the end of a trip, you must pay attention to many details. If you haven't flown IFR for a long period, you might not remember all the details, some of which can be deadly.

For example, buried in the first few pages of every NOS approach chart book are instrument departure procedures for airports with terrain and/or obstructions in the vicinity. If you depart an airport where the surrounding terrain isn't visible due to fog or clouds and you haven't reviewed the departure procedure, there's a good chance you won't make it to your destination.

More is involved in staying IFR current than just flying. How much refresher training should you get to maintain competency? The answer is probably anywhere between very little, for someone who flies regularly and stays current and a lot for someone who seldom flies either simulated or real IFR.

The instrument checkride includes more than your ability to fly an airplane on the gauges. Your knowledge of the ATC system, your aircraft, the FARs and how to read the charts come under scrutiny. If you maintain currency by regularly flying IFR, there's no requirement for any competency checks or refresher training unless you fly under FAR 121 (airline) or FAR 135 (air taxi).

If you fail to meet the six hours and six approaches in six months, you have another six months to get current, during which you cannot fly as PIC under IFR. After that you must be recertified by an instrument flight instructor, FAA examiner or authorized check airman (for commercial operations). Dual instruction or simulated IFR flight with a safety pilot in the right seat might be required to bring your performance up to the level where you can be signed off for further instrument flight.

We have friends who earned their instrument ratings but seldom use them. There's nothing wrong with that. We firmly believe that getting the rating improves a pilot's skills and makes him/her less of the mechanical type of pilot we seem to turn out these days.

Attitude Important

Much of how you view your competency and the need for refresher training depends on your attitude. Overconfident pilots usually do only what is necessary to meet the legal requirements for IFR flight.

Some pilots cringe at the thought of getting additional training. After acquiring the rating, they feel training is only for beginners. Others don't want to spend the money to hire a flight instructor to help them with problems they might be having.

Drawing the Line

We come back to the question of where we draw the line between legal minimums and competency. If you haven't flown IFR for 5 months and 29 days, would you go out in the soup?

The pilot in command is always responsible for safety of flight and this is especially true when it comes to your competency to fly on a particular day. It's expected that you won't fly if you're medically deficient or incapable of completing a planned flight safely. If you meet the legal minimums for IFR currency but know or suspect you can't handle the conditions that exist, for whatever reason, your obligation is to *not* make the flight.

For example, a friend took his airplane for maintenance to a nearby airport. The weather was IFR with a forecast of low IFR in fog. He took off for the 20 minute flight expecting to do an easy approach to the airport. But while approach control vectored him to the ILS, the weather deteriorated to the point where it wasn't an easy approach anymore. It took three tries before he flew the ILS good enough to see the runway.

He couldn't stay on the approach, since the last time he had flown an ILS was during a competency check six months earlier. This pilot doesn't fly IFR enough to stay current so he takes a comp check twice a year. He was fortunate in that he found he needed more experience than the legal currency requirement to be competent before he killed himself.

Changing Airplanes

Problems can arise when you change airplanes without a proper checkout. In these cases, the instructor often focuses only on the systems and handling characteristics of the different airplane, but won't include any instrument work. This can be deadly.

A pilot upgrading from a Cessna 172 to a Cessna 210, for example, will have his/her hands full. It will take many hours to get comfortable in the new airplane and become proficient in it. A good instrument checkout should be part of the upgrade training, or high performance checkout, for several reasons.

First, and most important, is the speed differential. Everything in a Cessna 210 will happen faster than in the 172. It will take time to get accustomed to the difference. Instrument scan must be much faster and include a larger and more extensive panel. If the 210 has an autopilot, that will help, but you can't rely on the autopilot instead of becoming proficient. What would happen if the autopilot quit during a low approach?

A pilot in the local area flew a Beech Baron for his employer, but wasn't instrument rated. When a larger company bought the business, he was forced to get an instrument rating for insurance and proficiency reasons. Although he did, he refused most IFR trips. When he had to fly IFR it was always with the autopilot. He was fortunate that it never let him down because he wasn't competent and the results could have been tragic.

When upgrading to a high performance airplane, you must learn a new set of techniques, such as when to raise and lower the gear, setting the prop, extending and retracting the flaps, etc. Add all that to a hard instrument day and it is easy for a pilot to fall behind and make mistakes.

What can happen? All the things you did as a student instrument pilot. You might fixate on one instrument, e.g., the altimeter, trying to get your altitude squared away while you lose your heading control because you still don't have a good feel for the airplane. You could concentrate so hard on an ILS approach that you completely forget about the landing gear.

Downgrading Problems

Another checkout problem is the pilot who is downgrading. There have been accidents where pilots who fly big iron get into a single or light twin expecting to fly it away. It has been many years since they've flown a light aircraft and sometimes they get into trouble immediately by overcontrolling it.

It is one thing to fly a large aircraft with hydraulically actuated controls, more than one crewmember, a lot of sophisticated navigation equipment and someone in the back to take care of the passengers. It's quite another situation to fly single-pilot IFR without an autopilot or flight director, little or no computerized navigation, and passengers interrupting by asking, "Where are we?"

The Value of Personal Minimums

Establishing personal minimums allows you to resolve the problem of what is legal and what is safe. Personal minimums allow you the flexibility to make future decisions long before it's necessary; when there's little pressure on you to perform. On the day the weather is skunky and you don't want to make a certain flight, you simply tell your passengers, the boss or yourself that the weather is below your personal minimums and you're not going.

There are two types of personal limitations. Fixed limitations are things that don't change, like never flying an airplane that isn't airworthy or one that's overloaded or out of c.g. limits.

Adjustable limitations are those you can change based on your experience and comfort level. For instance, there's nothing that says you must fly when the weather is forecast to be near ILS minimums. If you're not comfortable with approaches that low, your minimums should be established at a point where you feel competent. Always start high and aim low when it comes to minimums.

As you become more relaxed with minimums set at a certain level, and the approaches become easier for you to complete think about changing your limitations. Get a safety pilot or instructor to ride right seat with you the first time you fly in the lower weather conditions and listen to his/her comments afterward.

Other variables to be considered include wind conditions. How much of a crosswind can you handle on an instrument approach? Circling minimums is another. If you want more visibility for the circling maneuver at the end of an approach, establish a minimum for it.

Don't Cop to Pressure

It's important that you don't talk yourself or allow someone else to talk you out of your established minimums. If you do, your comfort level will decrease and your anxieties about the flight will increase.

When setting the minimum IFR requirements for currency the FAA had to consider all pilots, those who fly every day and those who don't. But remember there's a difference between currency and competency. Except for medical fitness, the FARs don't address the issue of competency. But following an incident, the FAA uses the 609 ride as the gauge of whether a pilot's abilities measure up.

It's incumbent on each of us when we launch on an IFR flight to know the conditions that exist, or that we can expect, are those we can handle. We have the responsibility to those we fly, and others on the ground, to complete any flight we undertake safely, without incident. That's where competency comes in.

• Section Three •

Handling Emergencies

Basic Emergency Guidelines

A *real emergency is something most of us would rather not think about. Why should we? It always happens to someone else. (Yeah. Right.)*
Knowledgeable pilots are able to cope with most emergencies. A knowledgeable pilot is a crew member who spends time discovering all there is to know about emergency procedures dealing with adverse weather, air traffic control, aircraft and systems, communications, instrument and avionics malfunctions, navigation, or physical impairment. More to it than you thought, isn't there?

We'll cover many of these subjects as this section unfolds. First, though, here are some general guidelines for handling emergencies.

Emergency Guidelines

There are several areas in which a good instrument pilot must have a solid base of knowledge on which to draw if he or she is to cope successfully with emergencies. Fortunately, most of these are based on plain old common sense and a realistic assessment of what you can accomplish:

• Have a thorough understanding of all pilot operating handbook procedures.
• Commit to memory all the emergency checklists for the aircraft you fly. If the emergency checklists are too involved, then memorize the items necessary to bring the emergency under control. You can then clean up with the rest of the checklist.
• Regardless of the possibility of a violation, take the easiest way out of a situation that could develop into a real emergency. This means

declaring an emergency with ATC and enlisting their aid. No doubt about it, if you're current on partial panel you can do it yourself and that's good to know if you ever need it. But why risk it? Remember the old saying about the superior pilot who does what he/she has to do without having to rely on his/her superior knowledge unless absolutely necessary.

A good example of this is lost comm. You've just departed and entered the clouds when your communications go away. What do you do? Most wet-behind-the-ears instrument pilots will recite the lost-comm procedures from the FARs, which say to follow your clearance at the last cleared altitude, etc. etc. etc.

Cripes, what *for?* You're practically sitting on top of your home airport! Set up for the approach in use. You can bet ATC is fervently hoping you'll do exactly that, and will make a great big hole in the sky to accomodate you.

• Advise ATC and/or an FSS of the situation and ask for assistance. If you can't raise anyone, transmit in the blind for other aircraft that might be within range, let them know what's going on and ask them to relay your problem and intentions to an FAA or military facility.

We were on a flight where we had just departed VFR from Nassau, Bahamas bound for Opa Locka, FL. We had filed an IFR flight plan and due to ATC saturation were advised we wouldn't receive a clearance for a very long time. After takeoff, ATC advised they could not find our flight plan. In the meantime, we heard an air carrier flight checking in with Miami Center, so we asked the flight if they would call Miami and get a clearance for us.

The airline crew called back in less than a minute and told us if we could climb VFR to 7000 feet, Miami would be able to talk to us and issue a clearance. Attempting to save face is the last thing we should ever concern ourselves with when we are faced with a problem that could get progressively worse. Help is out there and we should never be reluctant to ask for assistance.

Enforcement Worries

Many pilots worry about an FAA violation if they declare an emergency and an investigation reveals the problem could have been resolved some other way. We explored this with an FAA Accident Prevention Specialist and learned a few things about their policy and procedures under such circumstances.

A reportable incident will be investigated by an inspector to determine the facts. Any violation of the FARs will be identified and the pilot will be interviewed concerning his/her judgment in declaring an emergency and clearing the problem. The FAA will not attempt to second-guess what went on in the cockpit during the declared emergency.

If the pilot cleared the emergency using reasonable precautions protecting life, limb and property, deviating from the FARs will usually be considered justified under the circumstances. In other words, the pilot did what he/she was supposed to do. The FAA might want to look at the pilot's qualifications, currency, and background. They might also wish to examine aircraft logs, etc.

From the facts, the FAA will determine if the pilot should show cause why his/her certificate should not be suspended or otherwise questioned. This could result in a 609 ride and should reveal the pilot's competency to exercise the privileges of his/her certificate. The 609 ride will follow the Practical Test Guide for the certificate or ratings concerned.

Pilots should not consider the 609 ride as something that follows every declared emergency. It would be very foolish to even think about enforcement while coping with an emergency. The 609 ride is required if there is any question as to a pilot's ability to fly safely.

Constant Reinforcement

Coping with emergencies in aviation operations dictate a far different mind-set than any other experience we might encounter. For example, we must reinforce our thinking and planning since:

• Time might not permit undoing erroneous decisions, e.g., feathering the wrong engine.
• Insufficient fuel could force flight plan and/or route adjustments.
• Improper avionics set-ups and operations could create an ATC emergency.
• Lack of instrument and other pilot proficiency could make coping with emergencies difficult to impossible.

So what then is the mind-set pilots need to develop and reinforce? Prepare for emergencies before encountering emergencies:

• We must understand that emergencies are rare, but they do happen and we can never assume they only happen to others. The first step is to study and maintain periodic familiarity with the pilot operating handbooks of the aircraft we fly. For example, there might not be enough time to learn how to lower the landing gear manually during an instrument approach where a missed approach might not be possible or advisable.

• Thoroughly understand the ATC procedures and options available when communications and navigation equipment break down.

• Learn as much as you can about weather and always have a way out in case the situation deteriorates.

• Guard against spatial disorientation by regularly practicing partial panel and partial panel instrument approaches. Some pseudo-experts would have you believe partial panel instrument approaches aren't possible or likely; don't you believe it! They can be done and might save the day if other, easier options are not otherwise available.

More Guidelines

Differences between aircraft are important to understand when dealing with systems and equipment failures that could result in an emergency. As noted above, you should periodically review the pilots operating handbook to be sure you know how to cope with each type of emergency. In fact, it's a good idea to memorize the initial stages of each emergency checklist.

System Failures

Most aircraft are equipped with vacuum-driven heading and attitude indicators, and electric turn coordinators. If the vacuum pump fails, an electric turn coordinator and the pitot-static instruments provide sufficient information for safe instrument flight. It's important, though, to stay proficient at partial panel approaches in the event such an emergency occurs.

Safe IFR flight is also possible following an electrical system failure with only the pitot-static and vacuum instruments, but no navigation nor communication will be possible after the battery runs down. You must promptly reduce the electrical load to a minimum in this situation so you have some com/nav capability to fly an approach.

To fortify your options in the event of a total electrical failure, always know where VFR or the best possible weather is. You should know this before filing your flight plan and monitor the weather during flight. You can make it to a favorable location with only the vacuum and pitot-static instruments. ATC provides traffic separation in any direction you choose to go.

Subtle Failures

Here are two incidents that could have been disastrous. We were flying an ILS approach in the clouds at a busy airport. About one minute after intercepting the glideslope, we noticed that the glideslope needle was perfectly steady, as if glued to the center. We glanced at the VSI, which indicated a descent rate of more than 800 fpm.

We knew something was amiss even though the off flag had not appeared. This prompted us to level-off, and the glideslope needle was still unmovable. We told ATC of the glideslope failure and flew the localizer approach without problems.

Later, our avionics shop told us that a meter in the VOR head had failed. The off flag didn't show since the problem wasn't related to the glideslope signal itself.

The ironic part of this story is that a friend of ours experienced the same problem during an ILS approach some time later, only he didn't closely monitor the VSI. He broke out close to decision height, but wasn't where he should have been on the approach. It was a sobering experience. This is a good example of why you should cross-check all the instruments during an approach.

Comm Failure

Although a total communications failure is rare, you should be prepared for it. The most frequently asked question at instrument refresher courses is how to cope with two-way radio failure in IMC. FAR 91.185 dictates what you should do in this situation and ATC expects you to follow these rules (within the boundaries of common sense, as noted at the beginning of the chapter), so it's a good idea to commit them to memory. Let's review the requirements.

If radio failure occurs while on an IFR flight plan in VFR conditions, or if VFR conditions are encountered, you must maintain VFR and land as soon as practicable. Obviously, you must notify ATC after landing.

If the failure occurs under IMC and you don't encounter VFR conditions, continue the flight according to the following:

Route:
• By the route assigned in the last ATC clearance received.
• If on a radar vector, by the direct route from the point of radio failure to the fix, route or airway specified in the vector clearance.
• In the absence of an assigned route, by the route ATC has advised may be expected in a further clearance.
• In the absence of an assigned route or a route that ATC has advised may be expected in a further clearance, by the route filed in the flight plan.

Altitude:
At the highest of the following altitudes or flight levels for the route segment being flown:

• The altitude or flight level assigned in the last ATC clearance received.
• The minimum altitude, converted if appropriate, to minimum flight level as prescribed in FAR 91.121 for IFR operations, or
• The altitude or flight level ATC has been advised may be expected in a further clearance.

Leave holding fix/clearance limit:
• When the clearance limit is a fix from which the approach begins, begin descent or descent for the approach as close as possible to the expect further clearance time if one has been received, or if one has not been received, as close as possible to the estimated time of arrival as calculated from the filed or amended (with ATC) estimated time en route.
• If the clearance limit is not a fix from which an approach begins, leave the clearance limit at the EFC if one has been received, or if none has been received, upon arrival over the clearance limit, and proceed to a fix from which an approach begins and commence descent, or descent and approach as close as possible to the ETA as calculated from the filed or amended (with ATC) estimated time en route.

If more than one approach fix is established, you may select one and ATC protects the airspace at all of them. The phrase, "fix from which an approach begins" means any initial approach fix, or point at which the procedure track symbol begins as depicted on the plan view of the approach procedure. It would, however, be a good idea if you were aware of the active runway to select an IAF serving the active runway provided there's an approach available.

Urgent Situations

Some emergencies are distress situations, others urgent conditions. Some pilots are reluctant to report situations that could lead to emergencies, such as doubt about position, weather, fuel status or anything else that could affect flight safety. Ask for help before a situation leads to distress and bad decisions.

Emergencies involving weather usually result from inadequate planning, get-home-itis or lack of a way out. When you're in doubt about severe weather, it's better to land, reevaluate and modify routing or schedules than to chance an emergency. For example, unless your aircraft is certificated for flight into known icing, it could be suicidal to venture into conditions where icing is forecast and reported by other aircraft.

The same advice applies to thunderstorms. If you can't avoid them by 10-20 miles, land and wait it out. Always make your evaluation

---

The Ten Commandments of Safe Instrument Flight

1. Seat thyself well upon thy fifth vertebra, leaving not thy fingerprints on the controls and chewing not on thy fingernails.
2. Know thy instruments, for they are the true and appointed prophets.
3. Follow the indications of thy instruments and verily the airplane will follow along, even as the tail follows the sheep.
4. Do not stick out thy neck a foot; stay within the confines of thy ability and thou shalt live to a happy old age.
5. Know the appointed words and approved methods, so that if thy neck drapeth out, thou shalt be able even unto thyself to place same in it's proper place, upon thy shoulders.
6. Follow thy radio beam, for these ways are the happy ways and will lead to the promised land-ing.
7. Listen carefully, yea verily, to the signal impinging on thy eardrum, for sometimes they seem to have the tongues of snakes and will cross up thy orientation to the sad state to where thou must ask Heaven Herself for guidance.
8. Assume not, neither shalt thou guess, that thy position is such, but prove to thine own satisfaction that such is the case.
9. Boast not, neither brag, for surely Old Devil Overcast shalt write such words in his book and thou shalt some day be called for an accounting.
10. Trust not thy seat (of thy pants), but follow thine instruments. Read and truly interpret the word as given from thine instrument board and know that the responsibility lies not with the hand that rocks the control column, but in and with the mind that directs the hand, and thou shalt be blessed with a long and happy life.

---

based on the assumption that it's far better to arrive late in this world than to arrive early in the next.

The best way to handle emergencies is to avoid them in the first place. To help you avoid them, I've listed The Ten Commandments of Safe Instrument Flight, which appeared in a U.S. Air Force safety publication 50 years ago. We hope these ten basic guidelines will help your continued safe flying.

Some Flight Assist Stats

We often hear or read about accident statistics. What does not show up so often is the number of emergencies that didn't end in tragedy. This is hard to get a handle on, but there are some numbers out there to give you a rough idea.

The FAA *Air Traffic System Effectiveness Quarterly Report* lists data about how the FAA's internal procedures are working. Errors are pinpointed in the report which reveal operational errors or deviations affecting aircraft in the system. This is used to modify procedures.

It also reveals instances where aircraft may have entered protected airspace or airspace delegated to another facility or an aircraft that might have entered airspace at an altitude or route contrary to that previously approved. Further, it pinpoints instances on the ground where an aircraft or vehicle enters a landing area controlled by another controller without prior approval.

The report does not differentiate between airline, military or general aviation aircraft. Of pertinent interest is the section of the report entitled: Flight Assists. The assists could have been requested by pilots or the facilities themselves. The following chart reflects total ATC flight assists for 1991:

	Total	%
Lost	578	44.0
Equipment Failure	401	30.5
Weather Related	161	12.3
Low Fuel	113	8.6
Gear Up	60	4.6
	1313*	

*More than one cause is possible per flight assist.

We don't know how many of the above flight assists were aircraft on IFR flight plans or whose pilots were instrument-rated. But instrument pilots need to be alert to avoid some the same pitfalls that non-instrument rated pilots experience when IMC. The workload under IMC can further complicate coping with possible emergencies:

Lost: Positional awareness and paying strict attention to your flight plan progress will avoid getting lost. You must keep track of any ATC vector to maintain precise knowledge of where you've been and where you're going.

Equipment Failure: Good operating practices using POH checklists and checking equipment operation whenever possible before departure will all but insulate one from equipment failure emergencies, unless of course, something decides to break without warning. Coping with these latter problems can usually be successful if you have a good working knowledge of aircraft systems and aircraft manufacturers pilot operating handbooks. Familiarity with the individual aircraft equipment service manuals will also provide you with knowledge of how to cope and/or possible alternate courses of action to deal with failures before they develop into emergencies.

Weather Related: NTSB accident data indicate most of the instrument pilots involved in weather-related accidents where ATC flight assists were provided have been the result of inadequate preflight planning, pressing on where prudence would have dictated a routing change or precautionary landing before penetrating areas of possible severe weather and spatial disorientation. These problems have been exacerbated by get-home-itus which by itself, must be brought under control by all of us who fly.

Low Fuel: Some instrument pilots who have requested priority ATC assistance could have avoided placing themselves in jeopardy by carrying fuel over and above the FAR minimums. In the present traffic environment your options become fewer when winds, route deviations and holding consume more fuel than originally planned. If there's ever any doubt about fuel consumption or sufficiency of fuel, better to land and refuel before darkness reduces your options even further.

Gear Up: This category of flight assist has probably little instrument pilot involvement. But to be forearmed is to be forewarned. Checklists, warning horns and warning lights should give us some comfort. But instrument pilots need to be sure they understand emergency gear extension procedures and can lower the gear without having to refer to the POH after intercepting the glide slope. When your aircraft is in for it's annual or other major inspection, ask if you can extend the gear manually during the required retraction test. Very few pilots have ever gone through the emergency gear extension procedure except during an emergency. A little extra familiarity does wonders.

More to Come

The guidelines we've presented here only scratch the surface. In coming chapters we'll look at other aspects of dealing with emergencies, plus some case histories.

Trouble at ATC

W*hile not nearly as common as aircraft-related emergencies, ATC-related emergencies do occasionally
happen. We covered some in detail in the last book.
Here's a closer look at where ATC emergencies come from, and how to cope
when the problem is with the guy on the other end of the radio.*

Classifying ATC Emergencies

ATC emergencies usually fall into one of three categories:

• Those created by ATC facility breakdowns.
• Those created by aircrews.
• Those created by aircraft equipment deficiencies or breakdowns.

Facility Breakdowns

ATC facility breakdowns or disruptions are rare indeed; probably so
rare we take for granted they will always be on-line and working. Some
of our experiences with ATC breakdowns/disruptions during the last
50 years (yes, some of us *have* been flying that long) have been:

• Lightning strikes on radar, communications and navigation facility
antennas.
• Failures of telephone lines that support ATC communications.
• Power or communications failures caused by weather or construc-
tion equipment inadvertently cutting transmission lines.
• Computer disruptions.
• Unusually strong winds requiring personnel to evacuate the control

tower.

• Aircraft emergencies which resulted in traffic and communications saturation, requiring aircraft not involved in the emergency to be diverted.

We acknowledge these situations are remote, but in the real world they can and do happen. We must prepare ourselves against disaster by always having a workable contingency plan when we fly. We must ask ourselves: Are we proficient to operate in the IFR environment without assistance from ATC? For example, ATC's contingency planning includes the capability to go to a manual operation in the event of radar failure. If this happens one of the first questions you'll be asked is: "What is your position?" Positional awareness is a vital ingredient in flying IFR or VFR and must be religiously adhered to. You could suddenly receive the following clearance:

November-One-Whiskey-Echo, City Approach Control has experienced radar failure. Maintain 4000, proceed direct to the XYZ LOM, cleared ILS Runway 16 approach. Report procedure turn outbound and inbound.

Are you ready for this? If you have some doubts, find some non- radar instrument approach facilities and do some work. You could also request the full rather than visual approach when arriving at radar terminals. Even if the weather is CAVU, going through the IFR motions will reinforce your planning and procedures expertise.

Pilot Induced

Another testimonial for maintaining instrument proficiency occurred during an incident at a busy airport, where a pilot made several attempts to complete an ILS approach even though the weather was well above minimums. The disruption of traffic got so out of hand that ATC finally brought him down with an ASR approach.

An FAA inspector was waiting and, after interviewing the pilot, decided a 609 ride was justified. Needless to say the pilot failed the ride. Recovery of his instrument certificate cost him over $2000 and several months delay. Regular and frequent experience under IMC or simulated conditions would have made that expensive trip unnecessary.

Emergencies created by aircrews are, sad but true, not so rare (which is, in our opinion, another indictment of the inadequacy of FAA's minimum currency requirements). The majority of these incidents can be avoided by very careful preflight and en route planning. Many of these are caused by lack of instrument proficiency to include disorientation and inability to plan for the efficient use of avionics equipment in executing approaches, holding patterns and missed approaches.

Many emergencies result from encounters with severe weather that was accurately forecast. W believe many of these encounters resulted from a callous disregard for the elements and the all too familiar killer: Get-home-itis. Sure, the Weather Service will bust a forecast, but you must have an out for every forecast to avoid getting trapped and into an emergency. ATC will help when able, but don't put all your eggs in the ATC basket. Your own judgment should be conservative enough to guarantee safety from takeoff to touchdown.

Weather Analysis
Since the FAA consolidated and automated many flight service stations, more and more pilots are using DUAT and other automated services to obtain weather briefings. Although the FSS specialists are not weather forecasters, they have been trained by the National Weather Service and the FAA to brief pilots in a personal way that usually provides information not ordinarily found in a computer data base. Briefers have a feel for trends and have access to much more data than we do. This means pilots need to pay attention to weather systems and analysis.

Forgetting Details
Some instrument pilots still don't understand or have forgotten how to use the information provided in the instrument approach charts. During instrument competency checks, we find many pilots who don't understand that instrument departures at non-radar airports (both controlled and uncontrolled) require the use of an instrument departure procedure for obstacle avoidance after takeoff. These pilots believe ATC will automatically prevent them from running into mountains and TV towers on departure. Wrong!

Equipment Emergencies
Emergencies created or aggravated by aircraft equipment breakdowns are either pilot induced, caused by poor maintenance or by worn out parts and components.

Pilot induced equipment emergencies are mostly the result of lack of familiarity with the equipment. For example, we have flown with instrument pilots who have never studied the pilot's operating handbook on the flight director in their aircraft. You might say this shouldn't lead to any kind of emergency. This would be true but if for some reason the pilot had other problems which needed attention such as routing or destination changes, the flight director coupled to the autopilot might provide a safer way to sort out the details.

Maintenance Problems

With respect to maintenance, many aircraft owners wait for something to break before scheduling maintenance. The old rule, "If it ain't broke, don't fix it," has some validity, but with avionics, anti-icing and electrical equipment, it usually pays to have some attention given to peak operating efficiency before something breaks and creates an emergency.

One twin owner we know replaced his aircraft battery several times during the course of a year. He was replacing and recharging batteries at a fast rate and couldn't understand why. He had always complained that the ammeter was defective and he thought it was less expensive to replace and/or recharge his battery than have maintenance trouble-shoot the electrical system. Finally during his latest annual inspection, one generator was found inoperable, the other barely functioning, and both voltage regulators unserviceable. True, maintenance would have been expensive, but not as expensive or hazardous as a total electrical system failure in IMC.

Many single-engine aircraft owners and operators have installed back-up alternators and vacuum pumps. Something to think about if you are involved in lots of hard IFR and night flying. Another good piece of backup equipment is the hand-held receiver/transmitter. We have one and found it quite simple to navigate via VOR, including making instrument approaches. It won't, however, help you make an ILS approach.

Lastly, we like to carry one of the new-fangled hand-held GPS units. It can go a long way towards giving you peace of mind if your nav radios quit.

Close Encounter

We've saved the best for last. We've always placed a great deal of emphasis on positional awareness. Not too long ago, we were giving someone a check out in a new aircraft. We departed a TCA airport and were vectored toward rising terrain, which would have caused us to intercept a mountain and some tall antennas had we remained on the assigned course and altitude. This was on a TCA clearance and fortunately the weather was severe clear.

We informed approach control we were breaking off the vector and the reasons why. Had we been in the clouds we could have experienced a close encounter of the worst kind. We were operating in mostly flat terrain, where the rising terrain is gradual and somewhat further away from the airport than ATC normally takes us to exit the TCA. Because it was our home base, we confess we were a bit inattentive until we saw where we here headed. This could have been a disaster on the part of the controller *and* the PIC.

Avoiding the Trap

Personnel at the approach facility that handled us acknowledged they had forgotten us. They're taking action to see that there will be no further repetition of this scary incident. To avoid similar traps:

• Always carry up-to-date VFR charts, sectional or WAC's and refer to them often.
• Never accept a vector any place, any time unless you're certain obstruction and terrain clearances are adequate at your assigned altitude.
• When in doubt question ATC and ask for an alternate routing if necessary.
• Be aware of antennas that are being built taller and taller these days. For some examples of these monsters, check Fort Lauderdale, Raleigh-Durham and Nashville.

The ATC system has saved a great many lives and airplanes from it's inception. We should call on them when we need them. But pilots must also do their part. This means we must know our equipment, understand and abide by the rules and take the time and effort to maintain top level proficiency.

Overdoing It

A sizable portion of our training is (or should be) devoted to handling emergencies. The more complicated the aircraft being flown, the more intensive and extensive that training should be...which is exactly why heavy jet pilots and Shuttle astronauts spend so much time in simulators, honing their emergency skills. The axiom is, "After the simulator, flying the real thing is a piece of cake."

As with most things, however, it is possible to go too far, even in acting to deal with an emergency. This is the story of two medevac chopper pilots who quite simply overreacted, failing to engage their brains before their highly trained emergency reflexes took over. The story is presented from the point of view of Joel S. Harris, their instructor and one of our contributors.

Knowing When *Not* to Act

The two ATP-rated pilots had more than 15,000 rotary-wing hours between them. Both were military combat veterans and were experienced in the operation of the twin-engine helicopter.

They were on vectors for an ILS approach and were cleared to descend to the glideslope intercept altitude of 2000 feet. The ATIS reported a ceiling of 500 feet and visibility one mile in light rain.

Although it was a dark night, this should have been an easy instrument approach. The aircraft's flight control system was capable of flying a coupled ILS approach down to a radar altitude of 50 feet, while simultaneously decelerating to 70 knots.

Engine Failure
The sound of a loud bang, followed by a yawing motion to the left, were

the first indications of an emergency. Next the pilots heard the distinctive tone of the engine-out warning blaring in their headsets.

Both pilots saw the Master Caution warning lights in front of them, along with the red #2 Eng Out warning light. These were soon followed by the Low Oil Pres and #2 DC Gen lights.

The captain immediately reduced collective pitch to keep the remaining turbine engine within its operating limits. At the same time, the first officer pressed the #2 ENG OUT warning light to cancel the audio tone.

The first officer gazed at the array of warning lights confronting him. He seemed momentarily mesmerized by the Christmas tree display of red, amber and green lights.

Without saying a word, he looked up at the overhead throttle quadrant and grasped the engine control lever closest to him.

Wrong Engine Identified

After hesitating for a moment, he pulled the number one engine control lever all the way to the off position in one swift motion. The aircraft immediately yawed to the left and the engine-out audio tone again activated. He had shut down the wrong engine.

With the helicopter now in full autorotation, the captain bottomed the collective stick, removing all pitch from the main rotor system. By doing this, he was able to maintain operating rotor rpm, but they were in a 2000 fpm descent. He applied aft pressure on the cyclic, slowing the 11,000-pound aircraft from its 130 knot approach speed to 75 knots for autorotation.

The first officer, having recognized his mistake, depressed the starter button for the good engine that he had inadvertently shut down. (You have one guess what he was saying as he punched the button.) It took the starter 25 seconds to complete the start and bring the turbine up to idle rpm. The aircraft was descending in a controlled autorotation through 800 feet.

The first officer smoothly moved the engine control lever all the way up to the fly position, where the engine could deliver its full horsepower.

The aircraft was descending through 500 feet, in and out of a layer of scud. Although the pilot had full engine power available, he didn't use it. Unaware that the engine was again fully operational, he kept the collective pitch bottomed, concentrating on completing the landing in autorotation.

The first officer sat transfixed and mute staring through the windscreen at the up-rushing ground. Due to the darkness of the night and the confusion of ground lights, the pilot misjudged his altitude and flared too late. The aircraft struck the ground in a 15 degree nose-up attitude while descending at more than 1000 feet per minute.

As the simulator instructor, I sat quietly for a long moment and contemplated what had just happened. Two pilots, pros in their field, had just made some serious mistakes. That is what simulator training is all about—the opportunity to make mistakes safely, learn from them and not repeat them in the real world.

Lessons Learned

There are several lessons to learn from this scenario.

1. Know when to sit on your hands. There are very few emergencies that require immediate action. But many emergencies and malfunctions have been aggravated by pilot over-reaction.

In our example, the only immediate action required was a small reduction in power to remain within engine operating limits.

The pilots experienced what I would call a "sit on your hands for a minute" emergency. The engine failure was serious, but not life-threatening in and of itself. The aircraft was still flying, so what's the rush? Don't do something rash that has the potential to take you out of the sky.

The 15 Minute Experiment

In a study of flight crews using a Bell 222 simulator, pilots were given a catastrophic tail rotor failure shortly after takeoff.

The first group was instructed to land immediately upon encountering the failure. A second group was instructed to climb to a safe altitude and stabilize there for 15 minutes or until the pilots felt prepared to land.

Those instructed to land immediately crashed in more than 80 percent of the cases, while the second group crashed less than 20 percent of the time.

Think about that. The first group, perhaps feeling the pressure to do something even if it was wrong, was unable to cope with the problem.

The other group, having the luxury of time, was able to analyze and think through the problem, use the checklist and execute a successful landing.

When the situation permits, take all the time available, be as calm and deliberate as possible and use the checklist, since it will remind you to accomplish necessary tasks in a timely fashion.

2. Hands-on training. The pilots in our opening scenario could have given a discourse on single-engine procedures in their aircraft. This knowledge did not help them in the simulator. I have consistently observed that classroom knowledge by no means guarantees good results in the simulator.

When confronted with real-time problems, I often see pilots go blank, seeming to forget everything in which they have just demonstrated academic proficiency. In that unexpected moment of stress, you may be surprised by just how little information your brain seems able to retrieve. One way to counter this mental freeze is lots of hands-on training.

It is common to hear a combat veteran say that in the heat of battle a soldier may forget everything that he has been taught in the classroom, but he will do what he has been repetitiously trained to do. This true in an aircraft emergency.

What you have been repeatedly trained to do, you will probably do. Don't count on a clear mental process in the initial moments of an emergency. Very few of us are clear thinkers when fear and adrenalin surge through our bodies.

3. Communicate. Studies have shown that crews who communicate are safer than crews who don't. I teach crew members that no action in the cockpit should be initiated without communicating the action to the other crew members.

The crew in our scenario failed to communicate. The first officer should never have shut down the engine without the captain's concurrence.

He again failed to communicate that the engine he inadvertently shut down was operational again. The captain failed to communicate any instructions to the first officer.

Radio Confusion

I was practicing instrument procedures in a Lear 30 series simulator and was suddenly disoriented. The needles no longer seemed to point where they should and the DME was displaying confusing data.

What was going on? The non-flying pilot had changed nav frequencies without my noticing. Rather than saying something, he assumed it was okay. The point is that in a two-crew airplane, things should not be taken for granted. Let each other know what's going on, even if you're sure the other crew member saw what you were doing. After all, he/she might have been distracted and not paying strict attention to your actions.

It's a smart pilot who knows when to sit on his hands, and then lets them loose only to grab the checklist. It's wise to invest the time and money for regular recurrent training. And it's an intelligent captain who encourages communications in the cockpit!

Partial
Panel

Some of the emergencies that can befall an instrument pilot are things that, once they've occurred, the pilot can't do much about. Take catastrophic engine failure in a single, for example. Like it or not, you're landing. Now.

Other failures allow the pilot to press on, at least to the point of reaching VMC...we hope. One of the more demanding of these, and one for which we should practice a great deal, is failure of one or more flight instruments. The real danger is one of disorientation: After all, the gyros don't keep the airplane upright. It's designed to do that on its own. It takes confusion on the part of the pilot to upset the balance and cause real trouble.

In this chapter we'll take a look at two different methods of flying partial panel. First, the traditional "primary and supporting" method. Next, we'll discuss the "control and performance" method. Either will work, which is why we present both. Lastly, we'll take a look at individual instrument failures.

First up is Newton W. Miller on the "traditional" method of flying partial panel.

The Primary and Supporting Method

Partial panel—the very words chill the pilot's heart. The nervous applicant for an instrument rating shivers in apprehension no less than does the longtime instrument pilot seeking refresher training. Partial panel. What exactly does that mean? How is it done? (Why do it?)

Partial panel refers to those instruments that remain usable after your vacuum pump bites the dust. The standard instrument panel holds six little round glass faces. Three of the six are pitot-static instruments. Three are gyros.

Typically, in light general aviation airplanes, the turn instrument (turn coordinator or turn needle, as the case may be) is powered electrically. The other two, heading indicator and the attitude indicator, receive their spin from a stream of air drawn into the instruments' cases, directed at turbine-like vanes, and exhausted to the atmosphere by— that's right—a vacuum pump.

Vacuum pumps are known for unreliability. One pump may last 500 hours; another, 50. When the pump goes, so does the instrument central to a proper instrument scan: the attitude indicator.

It's partly for this reason that the FAA so heavily stresses the concept of primary and supporting flight instruments. The FAA method de-emphasizes the attitude indicator (AI). (Historically, attitude indicators were less reliable than they are now.)

There's no minimizing the value of an artificial horizon. It presents a stylized representation of the outside world, ground and sky and the line where they meet. This picture is enormously useful in both VFR and IFR flight.

Failure of the attitude indicator in IMC is troublesome both in practical terms and psychologically. Not only have you lost the yard-stick by which you make control inputs. You have also lost your representation of the unseen real world.

Recognizing Failure

First, let's consider how you know when that happens. There may be a warning flag on the instrument itself, but most provide no information on the health of their circulatory systems.

There is, however, a closely related instrument that will give you the story. You check it on each preflight runup, but how often do you check it when airborne? It's the vacuum gauge, and when your vacuum pump goes, so will the indication on the vacuum gauge. A practiced instru-ment scan that includes this critical monitor of your instruments' believability will sound the alarm even before the AI has a chance to slow down and turn quirky.

That quirkiness can be deadly. If you miss the first signs of trouble, the spinning gyro gradually slows to a stop. It's *gradually* that's the problem. If it quit suddenly the way an engine might if it threw a rod or swallowed a valve, you'd know immediately that something was wrong. Your horizon would turn over onto its side, for example. Because the gyro spins in carefully machined and lubricated bearings, its speed dissipates over a span of fifteen minutes. As it slows, it begins to lie to you. It can misinform you into loss of control.

If only the AI has failed, your instrument scan should reveal discrep-ancies between it and the turn instrument.

I was climbing through an overcast in a Piper Warrior 14 years ago and noticed that if I leveled the wings on the AI, the turn coordinator skewed, and vice versa. I chose to believe the AI (I was young and naive). When I broke out on top of the clouds, my AI showed wings level, while the real airplane was banked 15°. Misinformation like this can be deadly, especially if you're solid IFR for any length of time.

Keep in mind what your instrument scan is all about; it's not just to allow you to make smooth and precise climbs, turns, and instrument approaches. Your scan is also preventive: It's a defensive technique against the woes that mechanical defects can dump in your lap. You're looking not just for attitude information, but for correspondence among the instruments. When correspondence fails, an instrument may be in its death throes.

All right. The attitude indicator has died. Now what?

Initial Response

Pilots often worry about recognizing the defective instrument. In reality, it doesn't matter. You normally control the aircraft using the vacuum instruments: the AI and HI. If one or both give dubious indications, switch to your back-up instruments: the electric turn coordinator and the magnetic compass. Clear, accurate and immediate diagnosis of the problem isn't required. If one doesn't work, switch to the other.

There's a chance you won't discover the problem until the aircraft is on its way into an unusual attitude. The procedure is the same, regardless. Level the wings and adjust pitch until level flight is once again established.

The first thing to do is to remove the distraction that a skewed AI can cause. Cover it up. A business card works fine to hide the death mask of your dead gyro. I especially like those round plastic soap holders covered with tiny suction cups on both sides. Moistened slightly, they completely cover the glass and don't fall off.

With a dead vacuum pump, cover both the attitude indicator and the heading indicator. They'll both give you bad information, and bad information is worse than no information.

Once the airplane is level, and your pulse rate drops below engine rpm, it's time to fly the airplane. There's a temptation to start talking to the controller, but don't press that button until everything is squared away. Once you start talking, your mental workload increases.

Your next action should be to advise ATC about your problem. Although you don't have to declare an emergency, some seasoned pilots advise taking advantage of the extra help you'll get if you do. But at the least you should inform the controller of your loss. There are too many cases on record in which the pilot suffered loss of vacuum—and then loss of control, followed by a fatal crash—while ATC sat by ignorant.

Under partial panel, it's easier to hold headings and track airways for three hours to get to VFR than it is to fly even the simplest instrument approach. So when the controller wants to know your intentions, your intentions should be to get to any VFR within the range of the aircraft. If you can't get to VFR, your choice should be an area with the flattest terrain, the highest ceilings and visibility, and an airport with a simple instrument approach and a lounge on the field (just kidding).It might take some time to reach the decision as to where to take your emergency. But don't rush things. You have an equipment problem, not a time problem. Don't overlook the obvious. Why should you attempt a partial panel approach into a tight airport if, for example, you can go out over the ocean and let down to VFR?

Tips & Traps

Flight with only part of a panel really isn't difficult. The main problem is that we almost all get too little practice at it. The primary danger in partial-panel flying is getting into, and having to recover from, unusual attitudes. The obvious conclusion is to learn (and practice) how to avoid unusual attitudes.

The techniques aren't hard. To put it most simply, when the needle is centered (that is, the wings of the miniature airplane on your turn coordinator are level) and the ball is centered, you're flying straight: the wings are parallel to the horizon. With airspeed constant, your pitch attitude is constant and you're in stable flight. Probably the only really tricky aspect of flying with a partial panel is to overcome the psychological hurdle that presents itself, at least initially. Once you accept the loss and begin to deal with it, controlling the airplane isn't really difficult.

But turns complicate things. First, you have no absolute indicator of your angle of bank. Second, monitoring the change of heading on the magnetic compass takes a skill that many of us either never mastered or lost through long disuse.

The turn coordinator (to which I will now confine the discussion, since the turn needle is much less common) indicates the rate at which the nose of the airplane is yawing. It does not indicate directly angle of bank. To complicate its message further, it initially responds to the roll of a turn entry. When the airplane ceases to roll, and you've achieved the desired angle of bank and neutralized the ailerons, its indication is purely a result of yaw, or rate of turn. The rate of turn corresponds to a different bank for each airspeed. That is, angle of bank for a given rate of turn is a function of airspeed.

Are you confused? That's the whole point. The picture you think you see may be a fraud. In fact, the wings of the turn coordinator's miniature airplane can be quite noticeably tipped, while the airplane is absolutely wings-level. A tipped airplane on the turn coordinator means only that there's yaw going on. To prove this, take a look at the turn coordinator on the ground some time, when turning while taxiing.

The converse is also true. The wings of the turn coordinator can be level though the airplane is banked. All it takes is enough rudder opposite the bank to prevent yaw.

The point of this discussion is to make you look at the whole instrument. If the turn coordinator's wings are level and the ball is centered, chances are your real wings are also level.

Making a turn itself isn't too bad if you just plant the wingtip indicator on the index and keep the ball centered. The wingtip index marks standard rate, which is three degrees per second. Again, the angle of bank that goes with this or any other rate of turn depends on how fast you're flying.

It's wise when flying partial panel to keep all your turns standard rate, or less. Don't be in a hurry to do anything. Keep your control inputs smooth and modest.

Where to Turn?

The first question before making a turn on partial panel is, Which way?

This is not a trivial question. Normally you'd look at your heading indicator, locate the desired heading left or right of your present heading, and then initiate a turn left or right. Right?

Without the heading indicator you must use the magnetic compass. The compass is simple and reliable, but it's tricky to read, especially if you've just discovered that you're flying partial panel and haven't done anything with the mag compass lately beyond looking at it just long enough to set the heading indicator. Now the magnetic compass is all you have and the numbers on it read backwards.

A good technique to make certain you start your turn in the proper direction is to use the ADF card, to determine whether your desired new heading lies left or right of your present heading.

If you don't have an ADF card or something similar, remember this principle: The numbers on the magnetic compass slide downhill. When you bank the airplane (and the compass), the numbers on the upper side slide toward the lower side. Also remember that banking can produce erroneous initial indications on the magnetic compass. Never mind the complexities of these dip errors here. Just make the decision which direction to turn, then do it. Don't watch the compass unless you've mastered its idiosyncrasies.

How, then, do you turn to a specific heading? Or by a specific number of degrees?

Timing

Remember timed turns? This is why you practiced them. Timing is reliable, and it's usually safer than trying to relearn the peculiarities of the magnetic compass under duress. At standard rate, a 30-degree change in heading requires ten seconds.

In *The Instrument Flight Training Manual,* Peter Dogan recommends using half of standard rate for small turns. At one-and-one-half degrees per second a ten-degree turn, for example, takes about six seconds.

After you have decided which way to turn, you should decide how many degrees. Do this before you begin the turn. Calculate the number of seconds required. Then enter the turn, keeping the turn coordinator coordinated, and count off the seconds. Level the wings after the time has run out, and check the magnetic compass. Correct as necessary, but you should be pretty close.

Climbs and descents aren't hard at all if you have committed to memory the performance numbers for your airplane. (In this situation, knowledge of airspeed and climb/descent combinations for specific power settings can be especially helpful.) Add climb power and back pressure to achieve the appropriate climb airspeed; decrease power to the prescribed setting and let the nose settle for a controlled descent. (In either case, you'll see the result on the VSI and altimeter).

Perform one task at a time. Climb, or descend, then turn. Or turn first, then climb. Don't let a controller pressure you into complications you shouldn't try to handle.

What really brings the study of partial panel together for me is to analyze the correct response to an unusual attitude. Unusual attitudes are exactly what you're trying to avoid, but you must know how to get out of one quickly and decisively. What usually kills the pilot who loses the attitude indicator in the clouds is the crash that follows loss of control which results from an unusual attitude.

How do you get into an unusual attitude? Fear and distraction are the principal culprits. Fear can make your thinking muddled. Overcome this by learning the recovery principles so well that you won't worry over your ability to recover from an unusual attitude.

Avoid distraction by taking things a step at a time and also by letting

ATC know you'd like special treatment.

If you do find yourself suddenly looking back to the panel only to see wild fluctuations of airspeed and vertical speed, follow this simple plan:

1. Stop airspeed.
2. Stop altimeter.
3. Stop vertical speed.

Stop means to stop the needle's movement. The order in which you do this proceeds from the nature of the instruments, least sensitive to most sensitive. Coarse to fine. Some books will say that when the airspeed stops increasing (or decreasing), the aircraft's nose is just then passing through the horizon.

By the time you react, you are probably a little bit past the horizon position. Yet as you add the appropriate elevator pressure, the airspeed needle ceases to move. This is when you shift your attention (while still scanning the remaining instruments) to the altimeter. Its needle is probably still moving just a little. Note the direction of movement and add or increase elevator pressure to stop the altimeter.

Last, stop the vertical speed indicator. The VSI is the most sensitive of the three instruments and the last to stop moving (just as it's the first to indicate a departure from level flight). This final adjustment is the fine-tuning. You have nailed the horizon.

Be cautious about using back pressure with high airspeed (recovering from a nose-low unusual attitude). If the airspeed is high and increasing, too much and too sudden back pressure on the controls can lead to disaster. If the wings aren't level, back pressure will only tighten the turn; it could lead you into a deadly spiral. The first action when the airspeed is high and increasing is to level the wings. Then add back pressure gradually to bring the upward-trending airspeed needle to a halt.

If your airspeed is low and decreasing, stop the decrease right now! Don't worry about leveling the wings. Add forward elevator pressure at once to stop that dropping airspeed and freeze the needle. Then attend to the attitude of the wings.

Practice Promotes Proficiency

Practicing maneuvers while simulating a partial panel situation benefits your instrument skills in a couple of areas. First, it increases the likelihood of your ability to handle an actual partial panel emergency while IFR. Second, you are forced to get back to the basics of primary attitude flying which you probably have ignored for some time. A vacuum failure while IMC is no time to practice!

Now that we've sold you on the "right" way to fly partial panel, let's change your mind.

As with most things, there's more than one way to skin this particular cat. There's another way to approach partial panel flying, one that works just as well as the traditional method. We'll leave the choice up to you...either will work, so use the one you're most comfortable with.

Regardless of your choice, however, it won't do you a bit of good unless you practice it.

Here we have John Conrad to present the way to fly the "other" method.

Control and Performance Method

For the first several years of instrument flying, I had an almost overwhelming fear of having a partial panel emergency. The thought of having to fly an instrument approach to minimums on needle, ball and airspeed sent me into a cold sweat.

I wondered what would happen, if I took several minutes to figure out which instrument was in error and then made the wrong choice.

The result of this anxiety was a greatly increased workload caused by the need to continually cross-check the instruments to be sure that everything was okay. This incessant cross-checking is mandated by the FAA method of primary and supporting instrument scan and interpretation.

It wasn't until I changed my teaching technique from the primary and secondary method to the control and performance method that the transition to partial panel became easier. Not long after this change, an actual partial panel emergency proved the validity of the newer system.

The essence of the control and performance method of instrument interpretation is: attitude+power = performance. This seems obvious, but carries profound implications. Implicit in this statement is the understanding that if the aircraft attitude and the power setting don't equal the observed performance of the aircraft, you have an instrument failure.

Since the attitude indicator is the only instrument that gives a direct indication of aircraft attitude, it's the center of the scan. If the wings are level, the plane will stay on heading. If the pitch is correct, the plane will remain level. The attitude indicator is used to control the airplane, and performance is observed on the other instruments.

Subtle Failures

Let's review an insidious instrument failure and discuss how it is detected using this system. Imagine that your airplane is heavily loaded and climbing slowly to 10,000 feet.

The airplane seems to stop climbing at 9600 feet. You suspect a downdraft and continue to climb, but after a while you notice that the airplane doesn't gain any more altitude. In this case, the attitude plus the power doesn't equal the performance.

You're in a climb attitude at climb power, but no climb is indicated. In this case, you should suspect a blocked static system. When you open the alternate static valve, the altimeter, VSI and altitude encoder will rocket upward.

Vacuum Failure

The classic partial panel situation results from a vacuum pump failure. If you're like most pilots, your scan of the vacuum gauge is infrequent. If you are flying with the control and performance technique, your first indication of system failure occurs when the attitude of the aircraft doesn't equal the performance.

For example, you might notice that the heading indicator shows a change in heading, but the attitude indicator shows that the wings are level. Or the heading indicator might show a turn in one direction, while the attitude indicator shows a bank in the opposite direction.

Another possibility is that the heading indicator might not change and the wings are level, but the altimeter shows a climb or descent when the attitude indicator shows level flight. Under any of these circumstances, the indicated attitude doesn't equal the indicated performance so the transition to partial panel is required.

You may be wondering why I haven't mentioned the turn coordinator. If everything else works, this instrument need not be consulted.

With the primary and supporting method, the turn coordinator is frequently cross-checked to support the other instruments. While in the control vs. performance scan, the turn coordinator is a back-up, to be consulted only when something is amiss.

Furthermore, there is little need to consult the turn coordinator during turns. At any airspeed, there is an angle of bank that results in a standard rate turn. Once you know the bank angles for standard rate turns at cruise, approach and holding, the turn coordinator can be checked occasionally.

You might also notice that there has been no mention of the airspeed indicator. Once the trim is set, the airspeed takes care of itself. Unless there are substantial pitch or power changes, the airspeed requires only an occasional glance.

Perhaps the best payoff in using the control and performance method as opposed to the primary and supporting instrument scan is that your workload is one-third less than the workload of the latter because there are only four flight instruments to regularly consult whereas the other pilot has to consult all six.

Advocates of the primary and supporting method argue that if the vacuum pump fails, and the heading indicator and attitude indicator stop at an exact level flight and on heading indication, the pilot will be unaware of the problem.

This is true, but the odds of this happening are right in there with the probability of getting struck by a meteor at the outer marker. Since I have been advocating the use of this technique, I have made it a point to glance at the heading indicator and attitude indicator before I start the engine on each airplane I fly.

I have never seen the attitude indicator and heading indicator stopped on the correct heading with a wings level indication.

Transition to Partial Panel

The key to a smooth transition to partial panel is the scan that's used when everything is working. If the indicated attitude doesn't equal the indicated performance, something is wrong. The turn coordinator and airspeed indicator can be consulted for additional information.

The pilot who is flying by the control and performance method can instantly determine an instrument failure without the complex deductive reasoning required of the primary and supporting instrument scan where each instrument is supposed to be correct unless proven otherwise by the majority of the others.

Once the transition to partial panel is made, and the defective instrument is covered, a preplanned course of action helps slow the release of adrenalin.

Notify ATC of your situation and when they ask your intentions, you can get even with them by saying, "Roger, standby." Then recall your preflight planning and consider your options.

Fatal accidents after instrument failures prompted the FAA to require a partial panel approach on the instrument checkride.

A close examination of those same accidents reveals that, in over half of the cases, the aircraft had enough fuel to fly to either greatly improved conditions, or outright VFR. It can be inferred that the pilots either didn't know there were better conditions elsewhere, or never considered going there.

I recently conducted several instrument competency checks by the following scenario: I have the pilot plan a flight and I provide a full weather briefing that includes several airports with IFR weather and the possibility of reaching VFR conditions with the fuel on board.

The weather at the destination is always at or near minimums and forecast to stay that way. After an IFR departure, I introduce several emergencies en route, culminating in a vacuum pump failure.

None of the last 12 pilots I've flown with considered diverting to an airport with higher minimums or going to VFR conditions. All of them continued to the destination under partial panel, with results ranging from a successful partial panel approach to falling out of the sky.

I questioned the pilots as to why they didn't divert to better weather or go to VFR conditions. They invariably said that, because it was a training exercise, they assumed they should go to the destination and execute a partial panel approach.

Accident statistics show that most pilots in a similar situation fly over several airports with better weather while continuing to their destination.

The pilots on instrument competency checks who made it to the destination airport under partial panel, only a few asked for no-gyro vectors. Not surprisingly, the two who successfully completed the approach did.

I didn't fault the other pilots for not requesting no-gyro vectors. When on vectors, most pilots (myself included) have a tendency to focus their attention on compliance with the controllers instructions instead of keeping track of aircraft position. When the controller gives the final intercept heading, it suddenly becomes necessary for the pilot to interpret the magnetic compass and VOR indicator, then turn to intercept the course. He must shift from being led by the hand, to his own navigation.

Even under full-panel conditions, the point where the controller turns the airplane back to the pilot's navigation is fraught with difficulty.

In my own partial panel emergency (a double vacuum pump failure in an older twin), I elected to fly an easy VOR approach under my own navigation. The time spent tracking outbound and performing the procedure turn gave plenty of time to prepare for the final approach segment.

Rather than ask for no-gyro vectors, I asked the controller to monitor my progress and provide my position relative to the approach course several times. The weather was 1,200 overcast, with five miles visibility. Whereas, the weather at my destination was indefinite ceiling 600 overcast, one and one-half miles visibility in rain. The airport where I flew the VOR approach was 60 miles from my destination and the rental car cost $27.

Preflight Considerations

Preflight planning is an area where many instrument pilots fall down. Because of radar vectors, amended clearances, etc., many instrument pilots add up the miles and make sure there is plenty of gas. When they get into the air they fly the clearance they were given, at the specified altitudes, and generally do as they are told.

This works okay for a flight without difficulties, it omits the most important aspect of preflight planning; what you plan to do in case of an emergency. If you takeoff without a general idea of what you are going to do, or where you are going to go in the event of a partial panel situation, then you are asking for trouble.

Every time you take an IFR flight, take just a few moments to compare the IFR chart with the sectional or WAC. Then compare the weather en route and decide what you are going to do in case of an emergency.

When talking to the weather briefer, have him find you the airport along your route with the best weather and then see if that airport has an easy approach.

If you have a plan of action prior to takeoff, and if you can transition gracefully to partial panel, you'll be prepared for an emergency.

To close, let's take a closer look at non-traditional instrument failures; that is, situations where only one gyro fails and the like.

For this discussion, we've brought back Newton Miller.

Individual Instrument Failure

The flight from Sweetwater to El Paso was rough and tiring. Red dust saturated the atmosphere to 8000 feet and the continuous moderate turbulence made a chore out of merely holding heading and altitude. That was the day I relinquished fears about the structural integrity of the Cessna 150. I was tired; tired of having the radio knobs jump out from under my fingertips each time I reached for them; tired of tensing muscles against the incessant beating of the wind on my airplane; tired of using two hands to fly and needing three.

With darkness came blessed calm and El Paso over the cowling. My clearance into the pattern was routine. It was on final that the panel lights went out. I was set up for a normal VFR approach, primed to fly it by the numbers I had mastered. (I was a newly certificated private pilot at the time.) Airspeed was the key to a good landing. But to monitor airspeed, one needs an airspeed indicator. And at night, one needs light.

I had not yet discovered the mysteries of partial panel. I did learn something about partial panel, or should I say *zero* panel. There are more ways than one for an instrument to fail. While a dead vacuum pump commonly means loss of attitude and heading indicators (that's the FAA's definition of partial panel), there are other gremlins that can rob you of one or more instruments.

In other words, a discussion of partial panel wouldn't be complete without examining instances of partial panel that don't precisely fit the FAA's definition.

Vacuum Okay, But....

For example, suppose the attitude indicator itself fails, rather than the pump driving it (a common enough occurrence). In this case, you still have the heading indicator to guide you. Your response to this emergency should be to apply standard partial-panel techniques, e.g. needle, ball and airspeed. Fortunately, you don't have to rely on the vagaries of the magnetic compass.

Cover the attitude indicator, lest it confuse or mislead you, and use the altimeter for pitch information in level flight. Use the heading indicator to corroborate what you observe on the turn coordinator (or needle). Look for a rate of change in heading that correlates with the standard rate of turn that you'll be using.

The flip side is failure of the heading indicator by itself. Cover it and use the compass, applying standard partial-panel techniques. Now you have the chance to prove in real life what you learned during training. If you keep the wings level in coordinated flight, the airplane can't turn. That is, it *can't change heading.*

You've been taught to fly the heading. You can accomplish that by keeping the wings level. Since in this case of partial panel you have the attitude indicator at your disposal, that's easy. Just pay more attention to it than you would under normal circumstances. (You already spend 80 percent of your scan on that instrument.)

When I'm teaching instruments, I like to drive home early the connection between attitude indicator and heading. I lead the student through a series of questions: "What makes the airplane turn?" This question provokes a lot of wrong responses, the most frequent of which is the rudder. This leads to a discussion of the mechanics of turning flight. The answer I like best is, *the horizontal component of lift.* The question that follows: "How is that generated?" By banking the airplane.

Having arrived at the insight that banking causes turning, it follows that preventing the former prevents the latter. I make this point by covering the heading indicator and requiring the pilot to hold wings level for two or three minutes. Then I uncover the heading indicator with a flourish to prove that even though he or she has paid no attention to heading, it hasn't changed. *With level wings, the airplane won't turn,* unless you abuse the rudder.

If your heading indicator fails, it's just as if your instructor covered it up. Fly your heading by flying wings level. Use the magnetic compass as in normal partial-panel work. Trust its reading only in wings-level, unaccelerated flight. Time your turns, checking the compass before and after, then correcting slightly if necessary. Don't try to follow it through a turn and use it only for occasional reference.

There are other ways that you can find yourself with only part of the panel, other instruments besides attitude and heading indicators that you can lose for one reason or another.

False Airspeed

Two tiny holes connect the airspeed indicator to the outside world. All it takes is a bug or ice in the pitot tube and you have no airspeed indication.

But I have pitot heat, you say? That's all well and good, if you remember to turn it on before the pitot tube is iced over. (What if the heating element is burned out?)

If the ram-air hole of the pitot tube (or mast) is blocked and the static port is clear, the airspeed indicator behaves like an altimeter. As you go up, so does the indication of "airspeed." It can surprise you. Imagine that you have been in level flight for an hour or more; you've had a steady, unfluctuating airspeed indication. But ice has accumulated silently and insidiously on the pitot opening.

ATC says, "Descend and maintain six thousand." You add forward pressure on the yoke and roll in nose-down trim. But instead of the increase in airspeed that you expect (assuming no change in power setting), the airspeed needle remains rock steady. Then it begins, almost imperceptibly, to *decrease.*

This deceptive indication has led pilots to disaster. Thinking that airspeed is deteriorating leads a pilot to decrease pitch in an attempt to increase indicated airspeed. Pilots have persevered in this instinctive error into a fatal dive.

A blocked pitot tube doesn't always produce this problem. If the ram air opening is blocked but the water drain hole remains open, the pressure within can escape, resulting in a zero airspeed indication.

If you haven't mentally prepared for a blocked pitot tube and loss of meaningful airspeed indications, it will be unnerving when it happens. If you have prepared, you turn on the heat and wait for the ice to melt.

You should rely on your knowledge of corresponding power and pitch settings. If there's ice in the picture, you'll need to adjust power (usually more than you're accustomed to) as necessary to compensate for the severity of the ice.

Blocked Static Port

Few single-engine airplanes have heated static ports. Generally, this critical hole is placed where it isn't likely to ice up, but it can freeze over for other reasons, such as water in the plumbing. A definite indication of a blocked static system is a constant altimeter reading regardless of climbs or descents.

The airspeed indicator won't operate properly, since it displays the differential between static pressure and ram pressure. You can break the glass of the vertical speed indicator (VSI) to serve as an alternative source of static pressure if your airplane isn't equipped with a special valve for this purpose. The VSI glass is strong, so you'll need a substantial object to break it, such as a fire extinguisher, the screwdriver end of a fuel tester or corner of a metal clipboard. Don't rely on the VSI after breaking the glass.

If the airplane has an alternate static source, it's located inside the cabin, where air pressure is usually lower than outside pressure due to venturi effect. (It might also be higher; consult your pilot's operating handbook.) With cabin pressure below outside pressure, airspeed indications will be five to ten knots high.

The altimeter will also indicate higher than normal (10 to 50 feet), which means you are lower than indicated.

If you'd like to see the effect of air rushing past the cabin and tending to lower the pressure inside, take an altimeter for a ride in your car. Note the indication while cruising on the freeway with all windows tightly closed. Then open a window and watch the altimeter. It will jump noticeably higher, as much as 40 to 50 feet.)

The VSI won't work properly either if the static port is clogged. The VSI isn't even required by the FARs for IFR flight. It doesn't require vacuum or electricity to drive it, so it can't fail as the result of the malfunction of some other piece of equipment. It can fall victim to ice, however, just like the airspeed indicator.

With an inoperative VSI, cover it as you would any other dead instrument and use the rate of change of the altimeter as your guide. That's what the VSI is, after all, a rate-of-change-of-altitude meter.

Because you are using a source of static pressure other than that for which the altimeter was calibrated, it will read higher.

Loss of Altimeter

An altimeter can become erroneous with time, but it's entirely self-contained and requires no power to operate other than the pressure of the atmosphere acting through the static port. We've already considered how to deal with a blocked static vent.

Suppose you're solid IFR and the altimeter freezes due to a mechanical problem. You should confirm that the problem isn't the result of static system blockage. Then inform ATC and declare an emergency. If you have Mode C altitude encoding equipment, the controller can tell you your altitude, since the altitude-sending unit is independent of the instrument.

Without Mode C, ask for guidance to a location where there is a healthy ceiling under the clouds and level terrain. Enter a slow descent until you break out.

An alternative, should the cloud tops be not far above you, is to climb to VFR conditions on top. Then look for a way down VFR.

If your airplane has a manifold-pressure gauge, remember that at full throttle the MP gives an approximation of absolute atmospheric pressure. If you happen to have a table of the International Standard Atmosphere handy, you can convert inches (of manifold pressure) to feet msl at full throttle with a normally aspirated engine. Remember, one inch of mercury (or MP) equals roughly one thousand feet of altitude. It's not a great system, but it's better than nothing.

Turn Instrument

A failure of the turn instrument is another reality that traditional partial- panel teaching overlooks. The FARs require a gyroscopic rate-of-turn instrument, but you can live without it much more comfortably than you can without the attitude indicator, especially if you know what angle of bank gives you standard rate of turn at a particular airspeed.

Pay attention to what the actual angle of bank is when you have that miniature airplane's wingtip planted squarely on the standard-rate index and remember that the angle varies with the airspeed. You need more bank as airspeed increases. The bank angle required for a coordinated standard rate turn is about 15 percent of the airspeed.

Other Failures

This summary of alternative partial panels is certainly not exhaustive.

Besides the flight instruments, there are engine instruments that can fail and leave you with only part of the information that you have learned to rely upon from your panel in flight. Most of these failures won't affect the way you fly the airplane; however, they will dictate a precautionary landing as soon as practicable at the nearest suitable airport.

One lesson emerges clearly from the above considerations. Pay close attention to correlations between and among your instruments. Learn what they are.

Take note of the speed at which the compass card of the heading indicator rotates when you make a turn at standard rate in cruising flight. Pay attention to the angle of bank in a standard rate turn, and check the differences at both cruise and approach airspeeds. Watch how quickly or slowly the altimeter unwinds with a VSI descent of 500 fpm and 1000 fpm.

In short, try to become familiar enough with your instruments that you can infer the reading of one from the others. That way, when one fails, you'll miss it a whole lot less.

Engine Failure

H*ere it is...the Big Disaster. Loss of power actually isn't all that common, fortunately. Many more accidents are caused by the pilot losing control of the airplane in severe weather or getting fouled up and flying into something than are caused by the engine quitting.*

Still, it's the one thing we all dread. One of the scarier scenarios is losing an engine, in IMC, at night, in a single. There's just not too much you can do at that point. It's so scary that many instrument pilots won't fly single-engine night IFR for that very reason.

Twin pilots have it better, but not much. Some twins are a real handful if an engine fails during departure.

In this chapter we'll offer some guidelines on dealing with engine failures.

Engine-Out Guidelines

Non-pilots seem to be more concerned about engine failure than anything else when flying in single- and light twin-engine airplanes. They associate noise (engine running) with safety and no noise (engine not running) with catastrophe.

If engine failure were the grim visage it seems, nobody would fly a single-engine airplane in instrument conditions. Fortunately, the reliability of aircraft powerplants is legend and the incidence of complete engine failures so low that one-motor IFR operations are routine.

Most problems are caused by faulty components, not the least of which is the pilot. Fuel starvation and exhaustion accidents seem to continue unabated year after year, despite a lot of warning and education. The most stalwart defense against running out of gas in an airplane is no different than that used to keep from getting stranded on the Interstate...don't stretch the capabilities of the machine. Common sense and a conservative attitude should be applied every flight.

A complete engine failure in IMC is truly an attention-getter. How you handle this situation depends on what's left. If the engine that quit is the only one, you have few options. If there's another engine still grinding away, you have more options.

Single-Engine Considerations

What should be your first move when the only engine goes belly-up? Apply Flying Rule Number One: FLY THE AIRPLANE. No matter what has gone wrong, the finest emergency-coping is for naught if you lose control of the airplane. Despite what some of your non-flying friends believe, airplanes don't fall out of the sky when an engine quits.

When you've settled down after a sudden silence (this should take no more than a couple of seconds), go immediately to the pitch attitude that results in the best glide speed. Don't waste one second, since every foot of altitude preserved from decelerating is a foot you might need very shortly.

You'd probably have a few nasty comments about your luck if you hit a roof or powerline that could have been cleared if you had just a little more altitude. Don't leave that critical margin of safety several thousand feet in the air. Zoom if you can, e.g., use excess airspeed with a vigorous pitch change and gain as much altitude as possible while slowing to the proper airspeed.

Assuming that you've followed the checklist and power can't be restored, your actions depend on the weather and your distance from a suitable landing site.

Notify ATC of your problem (be sure to say MAYDAY) and one of the first things controllers will provide is a vector to the nearest airport. That's the best they can do in this situation. If you don't know how far your airplane will glide, put down this book and find out right now. We'll wait until you come back.

Most single-engine airplanes will travel two miles forward for each 1000 feet above the ground (some do more, some less). However, don't expect to roll the wheels on a runway 10 miles away when your engine quits at 5000 feet agl. The glide distance in the pilot's operating handbook is air miles. A lot can happen to wind direction and velocity on the way down.

If you're aware of an airport comfortably within gliding distance, go for it. You've nothing to lose by trying. A loran with a nearest airport search feature and constant read-out of distance and bearing is a huge help in deciding whether you can make it.

When you get there, don't give up one foot of precious altitude until necessary. Position yourself on a segment of a normal traffic pattern. By doing so, your perceptions will be of a normal landing approach and your chances of completing the flight safely will grow enormously.

Suppose your engine fails at an altitude out of airport range or in weather conditions that eliminate visibility all the way to the ground. You're now experiencing the losing side of the bet you made when you elected to fly in low-IFR conditions. There's little to do except set the pitch for maximum glide (for more time) and when you're within a few hundred feet of the terrain, slow as much as possible without stalling. The lowest possible forward speed at impact improves your chances of survival. You must also consider vertical speed, since compression forces from an excessive descent rate can hurt just as badly as high forward speed.

FLY THE AIRPLANE (Rule Number One) right up to the bitter end. Even if it appears that you're going to fly into the First National Bank, keep flying. It can't hurt your chances and it might help.

Multi-Engine Problems

There have been cases of double-engine failures on twins, but the odds against it are astronomical. If this should occur, follow the suggestions above and hope for the best.

There are three distinct situations to consider: takeoff/climb, cruise and approach. Each presents its own set of circumstances, but there's one thing common to all: when one of the engines stops producing power, airplane performance suffers.

The takeoff portion of an IFR flight is no different than a blue-sky departure. You must be cocked to react to an engine failure at two points during takeoff, prior to and after "refusal speed." We put that in quotes since the terminology varies considerably; some manufacturers call it abort speed, some refer to it as accelerate-stop speed and when you get to the heavy metal it's V1. Regardless of the name, this speed is the primary element in a chart or table that tells how many feet are required to bring the airplane to a stop after an engine failure on the runway.

It doesn't matter whether you're taking off into a solid wall of fog or brilliant sunlight, you've no reasonable choice but to abort the takeoff if one of the powerplants packs up before reaching that speed. Afterward? That depends on the runway length. If there's more concrete than the charted value, no sweat. If the pavement is shorter than the accelerate-stop distance, you're going to run off the end. It's important to know up front you must abort the takeoff if an engine quits before refusal speed.

Some of the larger twins come equipped with enough power to accommodate a continued takeoff once they've reached a certain speed. This is accelerate-go speed, and even though the chart says you can do it, you'd be wise to abort following an engine failure if you aren't beyond the accelerate-stop distance. The margins are so slim (none of these airplanes are skyrockets on one engine) and the conditions so demanding (immediate recognition of the failed engine, immediate retraction of gear and flaps, etc.) that few recip-powered airplanes perform adequately in this situation. Don't count on continuing the takeoff.

After Liftoff

Let's consider the consequences of an engine failure after liftoff when you've just entered the clouds. The first thing you'll experience will probably be a complete surprise: This can't be happening to me! Unless you've prepared yourself mentally, you'll probably start through the engine-out procedure like an Olympic sprinter coming off the starting blocks. Wrong, wrong, wrong....

The very first thing to do is (you guessed it) conform with Aviation Rule Number One: FLY THE AIRPLANE. There's nothing more important than control at this point. If you're so low that an unscheduled landing is inevitable, you're infinitely better off hitting whatever's out there with the wings level at minimum forward speed and a minimum sink rate.

If continued flight is possible, your adherence to Rule Number One will automatically accomplish the first step in any engine-failure drill. FLY THE AIRPLANE in this situation means straight ahead and to do that you must apply whatever rudder and aileron pressure is necessary to hold the heading and to keep the wings level (stand by, zero side-slip is coming up shortly). Now you can check the engine controls to make sure all three sets of levers are full forward (if you've already powered back to a climb setting, push 'em up to max power) and that flaps and gear are retracted.

When all that is completed (five seconds at most), the rudder pressure required to hold the heading gives an unmistakable indication of which engine failed...dead foot, dead engine. Continue to FLY THE AIRPLANE while you grasp the suspect throttle and slowly retard it. If there's no change (sound, feel, control pressure, yaw), you've confirmed the location of the problem. The next step is to feather the prop and fly on.

Here's where zero side-slip comes into the picture. Raise the wing on the dead-engine side not more than five degrees and hold it throughout the rest of the flight. This uncoordinated condition is now your normal condition and it's necessary to maximize performance.

Now you have time to clean up the airplane. If you don't have time to get the checklist out or don't feel you want to take your attention away from flying, don't be overly concerned. You've already accomplished the critical items and things like fuel selectors and alternators can be taken care of later. Do, however, make sure the failed-engine cowl flaps are closed. They're significant drag producers on most airplanes and drag is one thing you can do without right now.

Pitch Control

Attitude control is critical during this phase of engine-out flight. Unless you achieve and maintain Vyse, there's not much chance the airplane will gain any altitude at all. You might even lose altitude. The published blue line speed for virtually all light twins is calculated for an airplane at maximum allowable weight. If your airplane weighs less than that, a slightly lower airspeed will produce a better climb rate, but unless you know what that weight-adjusted speed should be, go to Vyse and stay there...it will work.

We also recommend very strongly that you establish the normal cruise-climb airspeed (well above Vyse) as early as possible in the normal takeoff sequence. As soon as the airplane is definitely airborne, hold the nose down and let the airspeed build up before you begin climbing. When an engine quits, a number of knots will bleed away while you're trying to figure out what happened, and if the loss starts at blue line, you're behind the eight-ball right now. Give yourself a break, altitude isn't nearly as important as airspeed when taking off in a twin.

Communicate

What about letting ATC know about your problem? What about conforming to your clearance? Both of these clearly take back seats to flying the airplane and securing the failed engine. A controller can give you absolutely no help. If obstacles in your path are so close that a minute or two of straight flight at a reduced climb rate will compromise your safety, maybe you shouldn't have taken off IFR in the first place. After everything is completely under control, you can and should let ATC know you've lost an engine and you're declaring an emergency.

Guess the controller's response: What are your intentions? It's a reasonable question and you should have the answer at the tip of your tongue, having planned for this from the beginning. The choices shouldn't be many. If conditions at the departure airport are at or above your personal minimums, ask for a clearance for the most practical approach available and tell the controller what your altitude will be (this is no time for unnecessary climbing).

If you've departed an airport with ceiling or visibility so low you can't return, your preflight planning should've included a takeoff alternate not far away with better weather and you should ask for an immediate clearance to your alternate. (We'll discuss the engine-out approach shortly.)

During Climb

As a normal two-engine climb proceeds, risk decreases with altitude. An engine failure during climb should be handled exactly the same as for takeoff with one major exception: don't climb any more than necessary. It's a foregone conclusion that any light twin will require full power to climb at all, let alone very rapidly, on one engine.

When reaching an altitude high enough for the initial approach (assuming you're returning to the departure airport), stay there and let ATC know. You're in an emergency and can have any altitude you want. Don't beat the good engine to death trying to climb. Level off as soon as possible, throttle back and give the horses a rest.

Failure at Cruise

If both engines held together while they were struggling to get you off the ground, they'll probably continue working well during cruise. But you know what they say about assumptions...

An engine failure during cruise is usually a lot different than a failure on takeoff or in the climb. Barring a complete breakdown of some vital internal part (crankshaft, connecting rod, piston, etc.) or your failure to properly manage the fuel system, you'll probably get ample advance notice from either engine instruments or your sensory perceptions (strange odors, weird noises, vibrations, etc.)

Whether the failure strikes like lightning or gives plenty of warning, Rule Number One is there to handle the problem safely and efficiently. If the autopilot is engaged when an engine quits, disengage it right away. It's not designed to handle the aerodynamic forces generated by the sudden onset of asymmetrical thrust and the autopilot could mask some of the control pressures needed to control the situation. You can, and in most cases should, re-engage the autopilot after things settle down and the airplane is completely trimmed in the engine-out configuration. Some autopilots are certificated for engine-out flight, so check the flight manual to be sure.

What Next?

Now, where to go? It's a critical question, with a number of factors to be considered. The proximity of a suitable destination is at the top of the list and, most of the time, the nearest airport with an IFR procedure and above-minimums weather (preferably VFR) is best. You'll continue to read about pilots who get into trouble trying to fly a crippled twin all the way home or to a larger, more convenient airport. So what if you rent a car to get home or miss an airline connection or meeting? When you've got two strikes against you, don't set yourself up for a third.

Power Setting

Now you must consider power setting and consider it very carefully if there's more than a few minutes between you and your destination. Each situation is different since you need to take several things into account, such as fuel remaining, altitude winds aloft, condition of the remaining engine, weather, etc. As a general rule-of-thumb, select a power setting that provides a reasonable airspeed while administering the least punishment to the good engine. Engine-out cruise is going to be significantly slower than normal flight. If you don't know what the approximate crippled-speed is, find out next time you fly.

Assuming you were flying at the most efficient altitude when the engine quit, stay there as long as possible. Altitude is like money in the bank now and you need to spend it wisely. In the extreme, you might want to fly all the way home at altitude and descend only when you're ready. Again, in an emergency, tell the controllers what altitude you'll maintain and refuse altitudes that aren't acceptable. Be reasonable, though.

Go to Plan B Now

An engine failure at cruise should trigger an immediate mental process, "I must consider Plan B, with the very strong possibility I'll need to implement it soon." If you're close enough to home or some other suitable airport to which you can continue as originally planned, so be it. You're now the captain of a crippled ship and you need to get to a safe harbor as soon as practical.

Remember, these two powerplants have probably been in harness side-by-side since they were built and whatever went wrong with the one side might also strike on the other. Just as you were taught the folly of stretching the glide in a single, don't push your luck in a single-engine twin. Get it on the ground soon and safely, then figure out how to get home.

Approach Decisions

Before you arrive at destination, figure out which approach will get you closest to the runway with the least amount of work and tell the controller what you want. This is no time to ask, tell ATC what you're going to do. The best choice in IMC is an ILS to a long runway, with a VOR approach the second choice or a radar surveillance approach, and an NDB approach at the bottom of the list.

A disturbingly high number of engine-out accidents occur after the pilot has arrived at the airport, is set for landing and loses control after allowing the airplane to slow below Vmc. Remember, the trim settings from cruise won't work in the landing configuration.

If there ever was a time for a stabilized approach, this is it. Once you've arrived in the terminal area, select an airspeed to use for the entire approach. Make altitude changes with small power reductions and retrim. Don't try and climb at this point. Refuse any such request unless it's unsafe to stay at your present altitude.

The most important part of an engine-out approach is the final segment, since you must get it right the first time. Again, select an airspeed (preferably slower than normal to have more time) and set the power accordingly. Make all power changes small ones and make them slowly to reduce rudder trim requirements and retrim. Fly a profile that requires only power reductions.

Flap and landing gear extension must be tempered with the power required for final approach, but if possible, configure the airplane for landing as early as possible during the approach. By doing so, you can trim the pitch and use small throttle adjustments to control the descent more accurately. You may need to use only partial or no flaps. Avoid a high-drag configuration, which requires high power, until landing is assured. Even then, a partial-flap landing shouldn't be a problem.

What if you get to the bottom of the approach and there's no runway in sight? The FAR 91 requires an immediate missed approach, but an engine-out go-around is a pretty dicey operation, if it can be accomplished. That's why we mentioned earlier that your first attempt must be a good one. The severely limited performance makes it more sensible to fly to an airport with better weather than to attempt an approach to minimums. A lot of judgment is required, but that's what you're getting paid for.

Failure on Approach

There are two sets of circumstances to be considered here. First, you've lost an engine during cruise and are now faced with an instrument approach to your destination. Second, one of the engine fails after you've started the approach.

In the first situation, fly the approach the same as you would with both engines running, e.g., same airspeeds and same configuration. If there were ever a time when you want things to look and feel and sound normal, this is it. You'll need to increase your normal power settings somewhat, the actual amount to be determined by flight test with one engine set at zero thrust.

The only departure from routine should be the point at which you extend the gear. It's wise to delay this until intercepting the glideslope on an ILS or when beginning descent to MDA during a non-precision approach. Gear drag will likely produce the desired descent rate at the same airspeed. You won't need to make much of a power change, which means you won't need to retrim; one less distraction.

No Missed Possible

From this point on, fly the approach as you would any other, including flap extension. Given the circumstances, a missed approach is out of the question. You need to make this one the first time around.

By flying a constant airspeed during the descent to minimum altitude, pitch trim changes will be almost non-existent, but you can count on significant changes in rudder trim with any reduction in power. Move the throttle very slowly and retrim as necessary. Ignoring rudder trim will find you holding a lot of rudder pressure in the final stages of the approach and landing, which does nothing but make your job more difficult.

Mid-Procedure Failure

If the engine fails in the middle of the procedure, there's not much to do but press on. Weather conditions must be at or above minimums, or else you shouldn't be there, ergo this approach will terminate with a landing. A missed approach with one engine is a very dicey maneuver in light twins and it makes no sense unless you're so far out of position when the engine quits that you can't recover. (And what are you doing there anyway?)

The indications of an engine failure will be much less pronounced when you're flying at a low power setting, but yaw remains the most noticeable. Rule Number One applies once again, and once the problem becomes apparent, your actions will be dictated by your position in the procedure. Still several miles from the marker on a vector or in the middle of a procedure turn? It might be wise to go through the entire engine-out procedure, clean up the airplane and fly the approach as discussed earlier.

If yours is one of those early twins with only one hydraulic pump to raise the wheels, think twice before doing that. A bit of power to overcome the gear drag is a lot better than going through the manual procedure twice. Most light twins will maintain altitude on one engine with the gear extended if the prop is feathered.

On the other hand, with an engine failure during descent to minimums, fly the approach using whatever power it takes. When you're certain which engine has quit, feather the prop. A windmiller is still the biggest drag item on the airplane.

Assuming the weather is suitable for landing, it's better to change as little as possible and continue. A go-around isn't called for and a slavish response to the normal engine-out drill (especially if push the go-handles to the stops) causes big, unnecessary excursions in pitch, airspeed, altitude and yaw. Recognize the problem for what it is and no more. Smoothly add enough power to keep the airplane doing what it should and fly the rest of the approach. If you don't have time to let ATC know what's happened, no big deal. They can't help you and you're going to land anyway.

One exception: if you haven't been cleared to land, get on the horn and tell the controller this approach will definitely terminate in a full-stop landing.

The Bottom Line

You simply can't discount the value of Rule Number One. Flying the airplane (and that means maintaining control in all respects) is the best thing you can do in any emergency situation, but it gets more critical when you're flying a suddenly-single multi- engine airplane in IMC. The only assurance of a positive reaction to an engine failure in IMC is to experience it under controlled conditions. There are simulators available for many of the light twins or you can have a flight instructor simulate failures in your airplane.

If your first engine failure in IMC is in fact your first experience, you may be in for the shock of your life.

An Ounce of Prevention

The best way to keep engine failure at bay is to demand nothing but the best maintenance and inspections for your airplane. This includes preventive maintenance between scheduled visits to the shop.

Statistics are on your side when it comes to sudden engine failure. It doesn't occur very often, being more likely that the engine will give some warning before it fails. A drop in oil pressure, rough running engine, unusual EGT indications during leaning or anything else out of the ordinary should prompt you to divert to a near-by airport or better weather.

It's much sweeter to be on the ground wishing you were in the air than to be in the air with a failed engine, fervently wishing that you were on the ground!

Communications Failure

W e'll close out this section with a brief mention of communications failure. What is of particular note here is that not long ago there was a change in the way we are supposed to deal with lost comm.

As we noted earlier in this section, the lost communication procedures should be looked at with a healthy dose of common sense. If you can safely get on the ground without following the letter of the law, by all means do it...ATC will thank you for it. It's a lot harder for them to shepherd you all the way to your destination than it is for them to make room for you to get out of the system along the way.

Coping With Lost Radios

Although communication emergencies are rare, they do happen and we need to fireproof ourselves with up-to-date knowledge of the regulatory procedures. Along with a review of the FARs, we will offer some advice for coping that isn't in the regulations.

A recent AIM change eliminates the need to squawk 7700 and requires a continuous 7600 squawk if you experience a communications emergency. This squawk code flashes on every radar screen in the area and alerts ATC that you have a communications emergency.

Receiver Failure

It's a sticky situation when you lose com/receiver capability in IMC and you can't get to VFR. If you've maintained positional awareness and the weather situation up to the moment of failure (as you should have), you must decide what you intend to do and transmit in the blind to ATC. For example, you could transmit the following:

XYZ Approach, this is November-Two-Three-Delta, transmitting in the blind on 121.9, squawking 7600 communications receiver failure, navigation equipment okay. Present position 26 miles west of XYZ at 4000, proceeding to ABC Vortac for the transition to the ILS.

Note: It's a good idea to maintain a listening watch on the nearest VOR for a response from ATC. If ATC wants to get a message to you that you're cleared, they could do so. It would be comforting to know they cleared the area for your approach. If you could do this, tell them the name of the VOR to which you're listening when transmitting in the blind. After ATC receives this message they will, after a little excitement, reroute traffic to accommodate you.

System Failure

A total electrical system failure under IMC is a very threatening situation. There are several things you can do to assist in coping with such an emergency. Conserve battery power by shutting down all but the most essential electrical equipment and decide how to get to the nearest airport.

Announce your predicament and position to ATC and announce your intentions or ask for assistance to the nearest suitable airport. If your battery is healthy and you haven't used it much after the failure, don't plan for more than 15-20 minutes of useful life, we recall one incident with a generator failure where we had less than 10 minutes before losing all electrical power. Fortunately we was VFR, but we had one nav, one com and the transponder on line.

If the failure occurs in IMC, we would shut everything down (including lights), except the one nav radio that would get me to the runway or to VFR conditions. ATC needs to know if you're operating at night without lights. If they can skin paint you on radar, they can keep other known traffic away from you.

It does happen occasionally: you could be flying along at night and ATC advises there is someone in the area reported without lights and they do not have radar contact to ensure separation. The smartest thing to do in this dangerous situation is to land immediately and wait until the emergency is resolved.

Com Failure

If you lose radio communications after takeoff and your clearance included a SID, you're expected to follow the SID unless you can maintain VFR. When getting a clearance such as, maintain 3000 feet, expect 6000 feet 10 minutes after departure, you're expected to climb to

6000 feet at that point if you experience two-way com failure.

Your route (provided navigation capability exists) should be:

• By the route assigned in the last ATC clearance received.
• If being radar vectored, by the direct route from the point of radio failure to the fix, route or airway specified in the vector clearance.
• In the absence of an assigned route, by the route that ATC has advised may be expected in a further clearance or in the absence of an assigned route or a route that ATC has advised may be expected in a further clearance, by the route filed in the flight plan.

Your altitude should be at the highest of the following altitudes or flight levels for the route segment being flown:

• The altitude or flight level assigned in the last ATC clearance received.
• The minimum altitude converted, if appropriate, to minimum flight level as prescribed in FAR 91 for IFR operations or
• The altitude or flight level ATC has advised maybe expected in a further clearance.

CAUTION: If you're on a federal airway with two-way com failure you need to keep in mind three things about altitude:

• If it's necessary to climb to a higher MEA, you may not climb until you're at the intersection where the higher MEA begins.
• If there's an MCA (minimum crossing altitude) or MRA (minimum reception altitude) along your route, you must plan to arrive over the MCA or MRA at the specified altitudes.
• MOCA (minimum obstruction clearance altitude) as charted means you can expect satisfactory navigational signals within 22 nm of the VOR. Be aware there are many airway segments where the MOCA doesn't allow you to navigate from VOR to VOR.

Transitioning For The Approach

Having complied with the en route rules for two-way com failure, how then do you make an instrument approach? If you have an expect further clearance (EFC) and the clearance limit is a fix from which an approach begins, commence descent or descent and approach as close as possible to the EFC. If you don't have an EFC, begin the approach as close as possible to the ETA as filed or amended. (This is another good reason for maintaining positional awareness and a how-goes-it according to your flight plan.)

If the clearance limit isn't a fix from which an approach begins, leave the clearance limit at the EFC time. If you don't have an EFC time, when arriving at the clearance limit, proceed to a fix from which an approach begins and begin the approach as close as possible to the filed or amended ETA. Although it isn't specified, we would use any initial approach fix (IAF) to ensure obstruction clearance and remaining in protected airspace. A fix from which an approach begins can only be, in my view, an IAF. If no IAF is charted, we would ensure adequate obstacle clearance can be maintained.

When in controlled airspace under IFR, you're required to report to ATC (if you have communications capability) any navigational, approach or communications malfunctions as soon as practical. Tell ATC the degree of your capability to operate under IFR in the ATC system and the type of assistance required.

We need to simulate the various com failure possibilities and think about how we would untangle ourselves in each situation.

Section Four

The Fine Art of Rust Removal

On
Training

In this last section we'll cover a variety of topics, ranging from general discussions of training to nuts-and-bolts discussions of how to maintain your proficiency and handle your aircraft better.

To begin with, contributor Brian Jacobson takes a look at the issue of training, itself.

The Need for Real Training

One problem I have with the way instrument training is conducted in this country is that not enough of it is done in actual IFR conditions. While it would be foolish to take a first-hour student into weather to practice confidence building maneuvers, when a student gets to the cross-country phase and is ready to go out and try the system it would be to his/her advantage to fly in marginal VFR to high IFR conditions. At some point before acquiring the rating, the student should experience low IFR conditions as well.

Conscientious instructors give their students the opportunity to fly in real IFR conditions, but too many others don't. I believe this results from our instructor corps' general lack of experience. In some parts of the country the weather is seldom IFR and much training is done in these places. Why is it so important that an instrument student get time in actual conditions?

Simulating IFR with a view limiting device works well in the initial stages of instrument training. The student learns the basics of scanning the instruments and integrating each gauge into a single picture of what the aircraft is doing, where it's going and how fast it's getting there. Once the student has mastered the basics, practicing approaches in VFR conditions is good for getting accustomed to the techniques required to conduct the various approaches. When a student can complete approaches with little or no help from the instructor, the real IFR world should be explored.

There are many distinctions between simulating IFR and flying in actual conditions. For example, the turbulence severity requires more finesse with the controls to maintain straight-and-level flight. A light or moderate rain beating on the windshield increases a student's anxiety. Low approaches, especially with any kind of crosswind and wind shear requires a new skill, one that should be developed with an instructor in the right seat instead.

When the weather is IFR controllers are busier, which often requires more of the pilot's attention during an approach. In some high density areas controllers issue a barrage of instructions to several airplanes at once leaving no time for verification or acknowledgment.

It's totally different to go out in VFR conditions on a crystal clear day when traffic is light and another to be in actual IMC during a busy part of the day. While it's impossible for an instructor to prepare a student for every possible encounter, flying in actual IFR conditions increases a student's confidence level. The world of actual instrument flying without a hood is very different from the one where a bored instructor watches a student fly one approach after another.

For years I've expressed the belief that it's beneficial to all pilots to get instrument ratings whether they ever use them or not. Why? A pilot who flies on instruments has to refine the feel and knowledge of the aircraft and its instrumentation to a higher degree than one who only flies in the VFR world. The skill that one cultivates while getting the IFR rating is a big plus when flying VFR. The pilot maintains closer altitude tolerances, as well as heading, airspeed and other parameters that normally would not be monitored as closely.

Rating Never Used

Notwithstanding all that, I know many pilots who begin an instrument course with the intent of using the rating to fly in the clouds, but once they get it they never fly IFR again. Let's explore why some folks are forever turned off to flying on the gauges.

Most non-professional pilots fly as a supplement to their business or strictly for the pleasure that tooling around in the sky offers. Many of them desire the flexibility that flying in most types of weather will offer, especially if they fly cross- country frequently. Having to spend three or four days of a vacation waiting for weather to clear while still halfway between home and a beach resort can influence the decision to start instrument training.

Instrument students soon learn that flying IFR isn't easy. At some places and at certain times the ATC system isn't tolerant of pilots who aren't proficient or lack the level of expertise required of them. We expect any pilot, professional or not, to have the same knowledge and abilities when flying in the system. Sure, the size of the aircraft or the equipment might differ, but the rules in FAR 91 apply to everyone.

Due to the complexity of the system the instrument rating is the hardest to acquire. The demands placed on an instrument student are many and those who drag their training out over too long a period have the most difficulty with it. Once the rating is acquired there are legal and practical demands placed on the pilot to stay current. It can be a very expensive ordeal.

Other than the compensation involved, there is one major difference between a professional and non-professional instrument pilot: the amount of time each spends behind the controls flying solely by the gauges. We call it proficiency. With some exceptions for severe weather the professional pilot flies whenever required and whatever the conditions.

As a rule non-professionals don't fly enough to maintain proficiency. While they may meet the legal requirements of six hours and six approaches in six months, keep in mind that those minimums apply to all pilots, those who fly in the system daily and those who don't. A pilot who was current on the first day of a six-month period, but doesn't fly IFR for five months and 29 days is still legally current to go out in the soup on the last day of the period. Will he/she be rusty? You bet.

What has all this got to do with the pilot who gets an instrument rating with the intention of using it but never does? A pilot who decides to get an instrument rating in order to take the family to their vacation spot in one day instead of five might finish the course and pocket the rating. Six months later, when vacation time arrives, the newly-rated IFR pilot knows better than to attempt the instrument flight. Despite constant self-prodding, he/she isn't current and isn't proficient enough to complete the flight safely.

Confidence Factor

Other pilots never develop a sense of confidence while flying on the gauges. There are several reasons for this with poor instruction at the top of the list. An instructor who isn't confident, knowledgeable and truly interested in the welfare of the student turns out a poor product. The first time he/she goes out and gets scared or gets chewed out by a controller for doing something stupid will drain all remaining confidence in flying on the gauges and in the system.

Instrument flying isn't easy. It's highly demanding. It will leave some people thoroughly sweat-soaked after a flight regardless of the cabin temperature. There are so many things going on at any given time that require the attention of the pilot. And the potential exists for so many things to go wrong with little or no notice. All this the pilot must be capable of dealing with on the spot with little or no help from anyone else. The reality of it scares some people away even after they have put the effort into earning the rating. At least they walk away from the gauges with a better feeling for and understanding of their airplane when they fly VFR.

Review in Actual

The flight review for instrument pilots could include some actual IFR flying if conditions permit. Simply putting on the hood and simulating an approach isn't enough to demonstrate proficiency. Conditions aloft are much different when the weather is IFR and the pilot loses the security of being able to take the hood off. Those who don't fly IFR often and consider the flight review a nuisance are probably the ones who need it most.

The instrument competency check is another example of where actual IFR flying would be useful. Broken up into two parts: the first could consist of an oral review and flight in simulated conditions with the second half flown in actual.

I realize what I'm suggesting isn't always possible since we can't arrange for weather conditions anytime we need them. A flight instructor or pilot who needs a flight review or instrument competency check can have time restrictions and need to get it out of the way quickly. But someone who is truly conscientious about flight instruction or the instruction received, will look for opportunities to fly actual IFR instead of looking for excuses to get the rides over as quickly as possible.

Another factor that needs to be dealt with is the currency level of instrument instructors. I gave some FAR 135 training to an experienced instrument instructor who was working with several students. He couldn't hold his altitude for more than 30 seconds. We had to go back to the basics and get him quite a bit of practice before he could meet the requirements of his instrument rating, let alone a FAR 135 checkride.

I'm certain this has a direct bearing on whether an instructor will take a student into the real stuff. Sitting in the right seat watching a student fly on the gauges might help the logbook but does little for the instructor's proficiency.

How do we better prepare our instrument pilots to weather the system, maintain their currency and their confidence levels? The key is to make the training, checkrides, flight reviews and instrument competency checks as realistic as possible and that means getting pilots out in actual weather conditions. Let them learn what it's really like to fly in the weather, what the system requires of them and most importantly what they must demand of themselves.

There isn't much we can do for a pilot who doesn't have the will or the financial ability to maintain currency. There could be underlying causes that generate someone's reluctance, such as the quality of training and the confidence level that was established while getting the rating. If that is so, we should identify whether the problems are the result of deficiencies in the training curriculum, if the instructor cadre is equal to the task and possesses a reasonable currency level or if instrument flying simply demands more than some people are capable of.

If the latter is the case than so be it. We cannot and must not compromise the safety of the IFR system in order to make it more amenable to the masses. But if there is a fault with our learning and currency system it should be identified and corrected.

We all need training, like it or not. And it can be expensive. But what's its real value? How much is it worth to pay for the best?

Here's helicopter instructor Joel Harris to make the case for going out and getting the best training you can possibly obtain.

Go Get Some Good Training

The value of good training cannot be overstated, nor can it truly be appreciated unless you've experienced it. After I got my instrument rating in airplanes, the first thing I did was find a cloud to fly in. The first approach I got was a localizer back course. I became so disoriented that I told the controller I had experienced equipment failure and needed a radar approach. I didn't tell him the only equipment that failed was the nut behind the wheel! I had been trained, but not very effectively.

This wasn't true in the U.S. Army, however. Although Army rotary-wing training was only 300 flight hours, it was the most intensive and thorough training possible. The balance of the nine month program was filled with intense academics. Graduation was a trip to Vietnam.

After 300 in-country combat hours as a co-pilot, I was promoted to aircraft commander of a UH-1B (Huey) with a crew of four. This was probably the most demanding flying I've ever done, and I survived after preparing with only 600 total hours. Excellent and intensive training prepared me, and thousands of others like me, for the task.

On the other hand, after I re-entered civilian flying I found most training to be inadequate to non-existent. One of my first flying jobs was a single-engine airplane salesman. The job consisted of flying airplanes around the Midwest to give sales demonstrations.

I once sold someone a new airplane and took a taildragger in trade. I had never flown a taildragger before, but the former owner convinced me that Once or twice around the pattern and you'll be checked out.

I later got a job flying helicopters offshore, where the situation wasn't any better. The helicopter to which I was assigned was known to be very difficult to land without experience. My initiation was to land on a small boat tossing in heavy seas 100 miles offshore.

When I arrived at the vessel, I was astounded to see the helideck heaving eight feet in the air with each swell. I attempted the landing rather than risk being criticized by the old hands. After landing, one of the ship's crew told me that I had come close to striking the tail rotor against an obstruction.

For the past five years, I've been employed by an aviation training company. We give very detailed and demanding training to pilots in the classroom, aircraft and full motion and visual flight simulator. I've learned more in the five years I have worked here about helicopters than I did in the previous 15 years since the military.

It's incredible how valuable good training can be. Unfortunately, it's expensive, and out of reach for many pilots. This type of training is attended by corporate operators or commercial operators where the customer mandates it.

Training is viewed as an expense by many commercial operators. The argument that one aircraft accident will more than pay for the cost of training doesn't sway them.

The difference between the trained and the untrained comes to light when a pilot undergoes simulator training for the first time. He or she may have thousands of hours in the aircraft, and be an excellent pilot, but are often shocked by their ignorance of the equipment and emergency procedures.

We're in the business of training, so an untrained person is our bread and butter. Nevertheless, it can be shocking when you realize that pilots are out plying their trade commercially who have very little idea about what they are flying and what to do if something goes wrong.

Quality training makes a tremendous difference in the performance of a pilot. If your pocketbook prohibits extensive recurrent training, make a disciplined effort to know everything you can about your aircraft.

One resource is the manufacturer. If you aren't sure of a procedure, for example, call the manufacturer and ask to speak to someone in the training department.

Everyone should fly with an instructor periodically. He or she (if they are professional) can quickly spot any bad habits. This is relatively inexpensive and should be considered part of the cost of owning or operating an aircraft. It has to be worth the sacrifice if you want to avoid becoming a guest star in next NTSB accident report.

The quality of training relies in part on the quality of the pilot, that is, the pilot's attitude towards flying and learning.

In this segment Joel Harris shares with us some of the personality types he's encountered in his work as an instructor. As we'll see, there are attitudes to be avoided, and others to be emulated if one aspires to true professionalism.

Good Attitudes

My career has involved military, corporate and commercial flying in both helicopters and airplanes. For the last five years, I've trained pilots in full motion and visual simulators. During this time, I have observed hundreds of the best corporate and commercial pilots ply their trade in the make believe, but surprisingly realistic world of flight simulation.

When I first my career, I heard the old hands talk about some of the marvelously skilled pilots they had trained. So and So could fly the box it came in, was an expression reserved for the very best. Whenever someone asks me, Who is the best pilot you've ever worked with?, I might name any one of several extraordinary aviators that I have worked with, or had the privilege of instructing. There are three pilots, however, who stand out in my memory. Of these, two have the well-rounded attitude that leads to true greatness. The third attitude will speak for itself.

Although I won't use their real names, I will describe some of the traits that seem to set them apart from the rest of us. I'll start at the bottom and work my way up.

The Joker

The Joker is by all accounts a skilled pilot. Like the perfectionist, he is in love with his trade and flies as often as he can. Unlike the perfectionist, however, he has had several aircraft accidents and incidents.

Although possessing an excellent control touch, honed over thousands of hours, he has never learned the old adage that there is a time and a place for everything.

I believe pilots enjoy humor as much as anyone. Perhaps it's a means of reducing some of the stress that can accompany flying. However, most of us know that the time and place for practical jokes is not in the cockpit. This is especially true during critical phases of a flight such as takeoff and approach. The Joker's flying ability and reputation have suffered from his incessant buffoonery.

Constant joking creates distraction. Distraction can lead to the neglect of cockpit duties and the neglect of duties can lead to disaster. More than one accident account includes a voice recording of pilots telling jokes or stories instead of minding the store. Flying is a serious and very unforgiving business.

The Perfectionist

More endearing qualities are displayed by the Perfectionist, whose motto is, practice makes perfect. He's a champion at flying because he uses every available opportunity to improve and perfect his knowledge and skills. He does this because he loves to fly and because he wants to be the best he can be at his profession.

He's like the football player who is always the first to arrive at practice and the last to leave. This type of dedication can only be rewarded. Many professional pilots reach a stage where they no longer want to fly unless they're getting paid for it. The Perfectionist hasn't lost his love of flying. He will pay to fly during his off time. This very experienced pilot often rents aircraft so he can go up and practice.

This constant work at his trade has resulted in what appears to the uninitiated as an uncanny flying ability. He can make an aircraft perform with an incredible exactness. In reality, his impressive skill is little more than the result of his long and faithful love-affair with flying.

Given the same effort, I believe most of us could develop into the pilot the Perfectionist has become. We all know pilots who like to brag about their expertise. But how many are willing to exercise the discipline and dedication necessary to become the pilot they imagine themselves to be.

The Natural

Finally, there's the Natural, who didn't at first strike me as particularly different from the other 10,000+ hour pilots that I've trained. I'd heard about him from other instructors and read the glowing comments in his training folder. But I was not prepared for what I saw in the cockpit.

The Natural is as smooth as glass. From the moment the session began, every maneuver appeared effortless. There was somehow no sign of the jerkiness that most pilots exhibit when confronted with the sensitivity of a flight simulator. The Natural's hands seemed to function almost as though they were computer-controlled hydraulic actuators. He would move the flight controls exactly the right amount in what seemed to be instant response to each new flight requirement.

His knowledge of aircraft systems and procedures are excellent. His cockpit management is exemplary. Yet, what really sets him apart from his fellows is this ability to be the total master of the aircraft. It becomes, it seems, an extension of himself.

I've tried to observe what this pilot does so differently from the other good pilots I've flown with, what puts him in a class by himself. Two distinguishing characteristics became apparent. They are focus and feel.

In retrospect I realized that The Natural's ability to focus is noticeable even in normal conversation. If you were to stop and talk with this quiet, unassuming pilot, you might be struck by the intensity of his gaze. You get the feeling that he is completely focused on what you are saying. This ability to focus is apparent in the cockpit as well. He seems able to concentrate on the various tasks involved in flying the aircraft, while shutting out unrelated and irrelevant activities. This ability to focus allows him to notice the smallest changes in aircraft performance and instantly respond to them.

I have already described his feel for the aircraft. The Natural does not make control movements, but rather seems to apply a constant, smooth pressure to the controls. Focus shows him what to do before most of us would notice. Feel lets him do it in such a smooth natural way, that the results are little short of astonishing.

Of the many gifted aviators that I've flown with, I have described only three, and all three have something to teach us. The Joker teaches us the seriousness required if we are to excel and indeed survive in the world of aviation. The Perfectionist shows us that discipline and dedication in flying result in superior airmanship. The Natural's focus and feel are something that we can all emulate.

Proficiency: Common Errors

Many of the contributors to this book series are *veteran instructors, some very veteran ("Students have been trying to kill me for years....")*. *As such, they've been exposed to just about every mistake a student is likely to make.*

In this chapter we'll present a collection of some of the common mistakes instructors see from instrument students, but first, it's time to take another test.

This one is designed to help you rate yourself as an instrument pilot.

Proficiency Self-Evaluation

Every instrument pilot who is serious about maintaining proficiency should be able to pass an FAA flight test at any time. However, maintaining a high level of proficiency can only be accomplished as a result of self-evaluation.

If you're reluctant to tackle an approach to minimums without the aid of a controller's radar and a fine autopilot, it's time to get back to the basics and restore the fine skill you had when passing the instrument flight test.

You don't need a flight instructor to go along during practice unless you would like one to review your work. All you need is an appropriately rated pilot who is willing to be a responsible safety pilot while you're under the hood.

As a starting point, we'll begin with an honest self-evaluation of your instrument skills. The tasks listed on the chart in this chapter contain elements that have plagued many instrument pilots at one time or another, regardless of experience and background.

Each task should be considered an essential part of a package of

skills needed for safe and effective performance under a variety of
weather conditions. Rate yourself on each task according to the scale,
which accompanies the chart. Be as objective as possible in your self-

IFR Proficiency Evaluation

___ Airman's Infomation Manual (IFR/ATC procedures)
___ Altitude & Heading (Always within]0' and 100'?)
___ Autopilot & Radar Vectors (Too much reliance?)
___ Avionics Set-ups (Departure, en route & arrival)
___ Basic Instrument Work (Without using avionics)
___ Charts (Understanding symbology)
___ Cross-checking Instruments
___ Emergency Procedures (Including engine-out)
___ FARs (Requirements for IFR)
___ Flight Planning (Documentation needed)
___ Holding (Clearance, entry and drift correction)
___ Intercepting & Tracking (ILS, VOR, ADF & DME arcs)
___ Missed Approach (Understood before starting approach)
___ Needle Deflection (CDI hit the stops during approach?)
___ Partial Panel (Needle, ball & airspeed approaches
___ Radio Phraseology (As per AIM, not "CB lingo")
___ Timed Approaches
___ An honest, overall appraisal of your proficiency

Rate yourself on a scale of 1 to 5 for each of the above tasks, where:

*(1) **Rusty** - Needs a great deal of practice and instruction before flying in
weather. Rarely practices and hasn't reviewed the FARs and AIM for some
time.*
*(2) **Below Average** - Needs practice; borderline; inconsistent performance.
Doesn't practice enough and knows it. Hasn't reviewed the FARs and AIM
recently.*
*(3) **Average** - Can safely handle most situations. Competent, but performance is minimal. May have personal minimums higher than published.
Practices occasionally.*
*(4) **Above Average** - Excellent instrument pilot. Can handle about any
situation. Reviews FARs, AIM and practices regularly.*
*(5) **Top Notch.** - Quality instrument pilot. No task is too difficult. Can
routinely fly to 200 and 1/2 with no sweat. Stays sharp and works at it
dilligently. Knows and understands the FARs and AIM in detail.*

evaluation. These tasks are the same ones presently required by the FAA instrument practical test standards.

Having rated yourself on basic instrument skills, see how those numbers relate to the following discussions of common mistakes made by pilots undergoing instrument training.

The remainder of this chapter consists of discussions by two instructors on mistakes they see made again and again. First up is Robert Davis, an instructor for PIC.

Common Misunderstandings

The pilot beside me asks, "Should I fly the needle or follow the controller's vector?" Another pilot believes that when the controller vectors him for an approach, he is being vectored to a procedure turn. Another pilot is confused when the controller says, "Maintain VFR."

With so many distinctions to make, is it any wonder pilots get confused? For the experienced instrument pilot who stays current, these distinctions become second nature. But for the beginner or the instrument-rated pilot who doesn't get enough recurrent training, the multiplicity of decisions becomes bewildering.

I encounter many misunderstandings among instrument students and instrument-rated pilots during refresher training and will clarify some of the common misunderstandings that I run across.

IFR or VFR?

A pilot who is not instrument-rated is always VFR, but a pilot who is instrument-rated may be confused about whether he is IFR or VFR. If the controller says, "Maintain VFR," you are not receiving IFR separation even when conducting an instrument approach.

If the controller says, "IFR control," or something similar, you are IFR and ATC is responsible for separating aircraft. Although, if you are able to maintain visual separation, you are expected to do so.

VFR and IFR refer to rules; VMC and IMC refer to conditions. The controller knows the rules by which you are flying, but doesn't know the conditions unless you tell him. The radar display doesn't show clouds or visibility.

Radar traffic advisories assume that the pilot is in visual conditions. If the controller says, You have traffic at 12 o'clock, and you're in the clouds, the usual reply is, We're solid, meaning, We're in the clouds and can't see traffic.

Altitude Reporting

When the controller says that the altitude of another aircraft is unknown, it means the aircraft is not communicating with ATC and is not reporting altitude. When the controller gives an unconfirmed altitude for another aircraft, it means the encoder is reporting altitude but the pilot is not talking to ATC. When the controller reports the altitude without qualification, the altitude is confirmed.

Pilots often wonder why the controller asks for an altitude report when the transponder is reporting altitude. The reason is to confirm that the altitude your encoder is reporting is accurate. If the encoder is off by more than 300 feet, the controller will ask you to turn it off.

Pilot Nav or Vectors?

Some pilots get confused about whether they are navigating on their own or receiving vectors. ATC can vector you to a published route and separate you from other traffic until you are able to intercept an assigned route.

The clue is the use of the word "vectors," e.g., "Cessna 5454V, vectors for the Monterey ILS Runway 10 approach", or "Cessna 736FB is cleared to Santa Barbara. After departure expect vectors...." Vectors may also be mentioned in a SID. "Resume your own navigation" and "Cleared for the approach" indicate that you should navigate on your own.

Approach Nav

A pilot navigation approach is one where the pilot is given a clearance to conduct an approach according to the route published on an approach chart without guidance from a controller. This route may be a standard procedure turn, teardrop procedure turn, holding pattern or a transition route. Clearance for an approach is either by vectors or pilot navigation. The controller does not expect you to fly a procedure turn after vectoring you for the approach.

Some approaches must be flown by pilot navigation where radar coverage does not exist. On Jeppesen approach charts, an R following an approach control frequency means that radar vectoring is available. In this case, the controller always provides vectors for the approach. If an aircraft is in position for a straight-in approach, there is no need for vectors. If you aren't sure whether an approach will be by vectors or by pilot navigation, ask the controller.

You can, of course, ask for a vectored approach, e.g., "Monterey Approach, Cessna 736FB with you at three thousand, ten miles north of Salinas. Request vectors for the Salinas VOR 13 approach." After the controller identifies you, he provides vectors and concludes with the approach clearance. This clearance has five parts: (1) your call sign, (2) your location, (3) an intercept vector, (4) the altitude to be maintained until you intercept the final approach course and (5) the phrase, "Cleared for the approach."

To ask for an approach on your own navigation, "Monterey Approach, Cessna 736FB requests the Salinas VOR 13 approach with pilot navigation." The controller replies, "Cessna 6FB, cross the Salinas VOR at or above three thousand five hundred, cleared for the approach."

Usually the clearance for an approach by pilot navigation begins with an altitude restriction and the phrase, "Cleared for the approach." This means that, after crossing the fix mentioned in the clearance, you should fly the approach as published. In this situation, the controller usually asks you to give a position report (such as procedure turn inbound).

Procedure Turn Vs. Straight-In

The purpose of a procedure turn is to turn around, get aligned with the final approach course and lose altitude. If none of these is necessary, you can skip the procedure turn.

Sometimes there is confusion as to whether the approach should be flown straight-in or with a procedure turn. This confusion can occur where the procedure turn is in the form of a holding pattern.

The thing to look for is the notation "NoPT" on the approach plate, which clearly indicates that a procedure turn is neither required nor permitted without clearance. If you don't see that note, a turn is required even if it seems that you can make a straight-in. Without the note, you should make one circuit in holding before proceeding inbound for the approach. The procedure turn is usually required in these cases if it would be difficult to make a straight-in approach and get established on the localizer and glideslope...either there's too much altitude to be lost or the turn is just a bit too tight.

Precision Vs. Nonprecision

A precision approach has a glideslope and the missed approach point is determined by the altimeter at a point on the glideslope called decision height or decision altitude. For a non-precision approach, the missed approach point is determined by timing, a navaid, DME or some other fix. The aircraft descends to the MDA and remains at that altitude until reaching the missed approach point.

Another distinction between precision and nonprecision approaches is how you determine when to descend. I am often asked,

"When do I start down?" On a precision approach, you start descending when intercepting the glideslope, but on a nonprecision approach, you descend when crossing the final approach fix or other designated fix.

Circling Vs. Straight-In

Pilots often ask, "How do I know when to circle to land?" This depends on the wind and the active runway. This is easily determined at an airport with ATIS, tower, etc. When the information is not readily available, you'll have to find out as early as possible and certainly be fore being vectored for the approach. It's important to know if a circling maneuver is necessary ahead of time, since the minimums for a circling approach are usually higher than for a straight-in landing.

There are four possible approach combinations: (1) an approach with a procedure turn and straight-in landing, (2) an approach with a procedure turn and circle-to-land, (3) a straight-in approach and straight-in landing and (4) a straight- in approach and circle-to-land. Once again, the solution is to obtain as much information ahead of time, e.g., wind, active runway, approach in use, etc., and when in doubt, ask.

Intercept or Proceed Direct?

The final cause of confusion among beginning instrument pilots is knowing when to proceed direct to a navaid and when to intercept a radial or bearing. When a controller says, "Proceed direct to the Salinas VOR," he wants you to center the CDI and fly it inbound. With an ADF, you should proceed inbound on as direct a track as possible.

On the other hand, intercepting a radial requires that you preset the radial and fly an intercept heading, usually in 20-, 30-, 45- or 90-degrees increments until intercepting the course. Intercepting an ADF bearing requires calculating the proper bearing and intercept angle.

Study and Practice

What can be done to make these distinctions become second nature? Study carefully any approach you plan to make. Anticipate the possibilities that may occur, depending on weather, wind and NOTAMS that may affect navaids. Fly practice approaches often, noting how these distinctions influence the manner in which they are flown.

Even when the conditions are VFR, file IFR and fly an approach at the destination. The more you fly IFR, the more you will experience the many subtleties that occur in instrument flying.

Now, for a different perspective, here's rotorcraft simulator instructor Joel Harris again with his collection of mixups.

Five Common Errors

Outside of the training environment, aviation offers little room for learning by trial and error. Failure to do it right the first time can result in anything from expensive aircraft repairs to loss of lives. In a flight simulator, however, we can make mistakes and not suffer anything worse than a bruised ego. So, in simulator training, mistakes teach us valuable lessons.

We can also learn from the mistakes of others without having to commit them ourselves. There are five common errors I have observed among instrument pilots during flight and simulator instruction in both airplanes and helicopters.

1. Failure to think ahead and manage time effectively

Five minutes from a fix, ATC issues Joe Pilot a difficult holding or approach clearance. Joe isn't sure how to enter the holding pattern or begin the approach, so what does he do? Typically, he continues toward the fix at cruise speed while wrestling with the entry or approach in a near panic.

If you anticipate a hold or approach clearance, don't be reluctant to request the clearance if ATC seems slow in issuing it. This gives you time to set up, configure and prepare for the execution of the procedure.

Of course, there are times when you cannot anticipate what ATC will do, or when you ask for an early clearance and ATC can't comply. In these cases, speed control provides additional time to solve the problematic clearance.

Slow the aircraft, then calculate your time to the fix. Now you can say to yourself, "Okay, I've maximized my time by slowing down and I have about eight minutes to work this clearance out." You have the edge psychologically and avoid the rush mode that makes calm, logical thinking almost an impossibility. Instead, you are in command of the situation.

Even with the additional time, you still might not understand the clearance or procedure. In this case, ask ATC for assistance. The AIM states that any pilot who does not understand a clearance should request clarification. I admire pilots who, when faced with a complex clearance in the simulator, are not afraid to ask for an explanation.

2. Forgetting to tune and identify all appropriate frequencies

The old flight school adage of "tune and identify" took on new meaning to me in the flight simulator, as I watched crews attempt instrument approaches while tuned to the wrong navigational frequency.

In this situation, the pilot is navigating on a victor airway when ATC clears him or her for an ILS approach at the destination airport. The pilot doesn't tune the localizer and doesn't pick up on cues that signal the error, such as glideslope flag, ADF bearing pointer, and CDI sensitivity.

Could this really happen? The crew of a Beech 99, with 12 passengers aboard, tried to shoot the ILS to Shenandoah Valley Airport, Virginia without retuning the nav radio from the en route VOR frequency.

In this case, the VOR used for navigation was off the field, and the final approach course was 045°. The NTSB concluded that the crew intercepted the 045-degree radial from the VOR thinking that they were on the inbound localizer course. Unfortunately, the parallel course provided by the VOR terminated in the side of a mountain, resulting in the deaths of all on board.

Tuning and identifying frequencies may sound like a flight school cliche, but in fact it's a life-saving habit.

3. Lack of situational awareness

This is also known as the "If ATC knows where I am, why should I worry?" syndrome. Situational awareness means knowing where you are, where you're going, and what's going on around you. Consistently good situational awareness is an earmark of the best instrument pilots.

One of the accidents we noted in the last book in this series (*IFR Accidents,* page 33) illustrated the need for good IFR situational awareness. In this case, ATC mistakenly vectored the aircraft into a mountainside during an approach. If the pilot had been aware of his position, he would have realized that the vector to intercept the approach course took him away from the airport.

Poor situational awareness usually results from failure to use the tools available to establish orientation. For example, when shooting an ILS approach to an airport that also has a Vortac, I find it helpful to:

• Tune the Vortac and put the DME in hold in order to continue to get distance information after retuning the localizer.
• Tune the LOM and slave a bearing pointer to it, so I know my position relative to this navaid.
• When using a horizontal situation indicator (HSI), select the inbound course as soon as possible. An HSI does just what its name implies. It depicts the aircraft's horizontal situation relative to the approach being flown.

4. Misreading NOS approach chart minimums

Many pilots overlook the lower minimums when using an NOS chart for an approach with separate DME or dual VOR minimums. This occurs because NOS depicts DME and dual VOR minimums in a separate section below the straight-in minimums. Your eyes naturally look first to the higher straight-in minimums. Unless you have reviewed the chart, or are aware of this NOS gotcha, you will probably use the higher minimums.

5. Not looking for the runway until the missed approach point

This error is committed both by single-pilot and two-pilot IFR crews. In the multi-crew situation, the pilot flying the aircraft on an instrument approach is absorbed with interpreting the instruments and controlling the aircraft.

Meanwhile, the pilot not flying is busy giving altitude and course deviation calls, reviewing the MDA or DH, double-checking that the gear is down and confirming the missed approach point. Then, just prior to the MAP, the pilot not flying looks out the window to see if the runway is in sight.

For some approaches, the MAP is far down the runway or is over the threshold at a relatively high altitude. (For examples of this, see Volume 4 of the series, *On The Approach.*) If the runway is not in sight prior to that point, a landing using normal descent rates and normal bank angles is unlikely, even for helicopters.

Many times, sitting in the back of the simulator, I can see the approaching runway for as long as a minute while the crew is busy with checks and double-checks, unaware that the runway is in sight.

The mistakes we make and survive can be our most valuable learning experiences. The best pilots are not those who claim to be error-free, but those who admit their mistakes and learn from them.

Instrument Scanning

While IFR, we rely entirely on the instruments to keep us shiny-side-up and headed in the right direction. That requires us to keep everything nice and tidy, with all the pointers in the correct spot.

The tried-and-true method of doing this is, naturally, the instrument scan. We talked a bit about scanning in the chapter on partial panel flying. Let's take a closer look, starting with a general discussion of scanning and followed by a more specific set of scan techniques.

Scan Wars

You'd think that with all the training time and effort spent on it, scanning would be thoroughly second-nature to us, like reading a page or handling a knife and fork—a skill that comes back fresh whenever we need it.

Yet when instrument pilots seek refresher training, their foremost complaint (or instructor-diagnosed problem) is that "my plane and I don't understand each other." What often drives us to seek retraining is our worry over being constantly surprised in little or big ways by flying machines that refuse to act orderly and predictably. As we often put it, the airplane gets ahead of us and stays ahead.

While in clouds, the rusty pilot sees him or herself not as the manager of orderly, well-behaved needles registering harmony. Rather, he or she may feel like a novice schoolteacher overseeing a playground full of hyperactive, mischievous kids, each of whom plays a different game by different rules. He or she knows to keep a sharp eye on the general scene, but is uncertain about which kids (read: gauges) need the closest watching or just what is going on when he/she sees it.

Failure at High Levels

For some pilots, a good scan seems to come naturally, but it is really a habit born of constant practice. For many others, scanning quickly deteriorates into a sometime thing as neglect, forgetfulness and/or fatigue erode their skill. Instead of following their best resolves and instincts, they commit errors of fixation and omission, while their aircraft wander among various altitudes and headings.

Why should this be? Maintaining a good scan of all the instruments is not vigorous physical or intellectual work. When done well, it makes flying easier. Why is it so often neglected, even at times by professionals?In 1985, the captain of a B-747SP (while IMC) lost an engine, misinterpreted his flight and engine instruments and relied too long on the autopilot. Though he had no real idea of the airplane's situation, when he took the controls, he worked them desperately to reorient the airplane. He put the 747 through a complete roll in a near vertical attitude, after which the 747 dove at 20,000 fpm before breaking out! The pilot managed to regain control of the airplane and made a safe landing.

The flight data recorder revealed that had he scanned the panel and properly interpreted the instruments, he could have perceived the real situation and prevented injury to his passengers and damage to the airplane. Instead, he based his judgments essentially on the engine gauges, a lessening airspeed and the attitude indicator; which, for no good reason, he inferred had failed.

The pilot placed so much reliance on the autopilot and the secure feeling of a routine operation that when the engine hung up and the 747's performance changed, he was so far out of the control loop that he overlooked obvious and correct indications.

In composite, here were the basic scan failures:

• The pilot concentrates on (stares at) only a portion of the panel, perhaps only one or two instruments.
• The pilot concentrates on only one task at a time, while others demand attention.
• The pilot draws final conclusions from the partial scan, though vital information has been omitted from his scan.
• The pilot takes the airplane, the situation and the instrument readings for granted without close monitoring at all times.
• The pilot misinterprets a gauge and fails to seek confirmatory or contradictory information elsewhere.

Basic faults, and common ones at that.

Some Reasons for Failure

Scanning demands both concentration and a departure from how we normally do things that demand concentration. People usually perform tasks one or two items at a time. When several tasks must be accomplished, we typically put some of them on the back burner until more pressing ones are handled. Even when we drive, our tasks, which range from watching the road to monitoring the fuel to talking to passengers, are unconsciously put in a certain order of priority so that our main concentration is on the road and other cars.

We write this thing or read that thing or turn this screw or adjust that knob and check the results and then go on to the next task. We focus, do and then shift our focus to do something else.

Flying on instruments departs from that usual way of concentration. Many things simultaneously demand our attention: flying a procedure (such as following a SID) can involve many tasks. Not only must we fly the published headings and altitudes, which involves reading and rereading several instruments and handling the controls accordingly, but we must monitor other instruments, switch frequencies, listen and/ or talk to ATC, copy a clearance amendment, etc.

Reading and interpreting each instrument is in itself a task that must be done in conjunction with others, over and over.

In short, you should not handle tasks like a fielder or a batter, by keeping your eye fixed on the ball. You should handle them something like a juggler, watching several balls together. Even while emphasizing one task, such as initiating a climb or capturing a glideslope, you must maintain a broad concentration. The focus must be on the whole airplane, using the eyes as guidance.

Continuous Change

An airplane moves in three dimensions simultaneously and is constantly changing in small ways as it responds to the atmosphere, control inputs and gradually altering weight and balance. Even the most finely trimmed airplane will stray, and, in the clouds, only the gauges can tell the story about changes in pitch, bank, yaw, altitude, airspeed and heading.

Good instrument flying is a process of continuously detecting the onset of unwanted changes and countering them before they become noticeable, all the while that you manage desired changes or maintain general stability.

For example, if you want to turn to a new heading but want to maintain altitude, your task is to bank to a desired angle, hold the bank for a certain duration and then roll out to level at the new heading, all the while maintaining a level pitch or managing it so that you remain at a given altitude. Managing will probably mean making several tiny pressure adjustments as you see the nose dot in your attitude indicator waver and as you may also see the needle of your vertical speed indicator begin to move up or down. The trick is to be there with an answer as the unwanted change begins, all the while that you are bringing about a desired change. For that, you must focus on the whole airplane.

Strangely, in a relatively easy case such as this, fixation can take three forms. First, you could so concentrate on turning to the new heading that you concentrate on the heading indicator after banking, thus neglecting the attitude indicator and other instruments. Second, You could concentrate on the bank aspect of the AI and on the heading indicator (HI) and overlook all indications of pitch and altitude change. Third, on seeing a need to correct the pitch or arrest a climb or descent, you could start to neglect bank angle and heading change during the turn.

All these forms of fixation reflect a narrowness rather than a breadth of focus. In level flight, your focus might be on maintaining heading and altitude, but for very long periods neglect to scan such vital gauges as those governing fuel, oil, suction and electrical output. Pilots have lost valuable time and other advantages in emergencies for having neglected to notice the onset of fuel, vacuum or electrical power loss reflected by those peripheral indicators.

Taking Proper Notice

Two other types of scan omission were demonstrated by the unfortunate 747 pilot mentioned earlier. Apparently, when the crisis first hit, he was bewildered by what was happening. Then, in deciding that his attitude indicator had failed, he was not registering its message; his copilot's AI read the same as his, and, furthermore, his AI showed no flag or other sign of failure.

Your scan can fail if you fail to look at the whole panel out of laziness or fatigue. It can fail if you let your eyes run over the instruments without actually reading them.

Fatigue and other stresses have a lot to do with this problem. A conscientious pilot reads the panel innumerable times on even a short flight. There is consequently a great temptation to take successive readings for granted. If everything remains normal and routine, boredom, complacency and fatigue may dull your perceptions. They may irritate you or stir your impatience to where you will see the indications not as they are as they begin to deviate but as you have been seeing them and expect to continue seeing them.

So affected, your vision may tunnel, so that you scan only a portion of the gauges. You may fail to notice that the airplane is in a slight bank and that the HI has been indicating a gently changing heading. You may also overlook that the CDI has moved off center by a dot or two and is still drifting wide.

Similarly, if you concentrate on maintaining heading or making an intercept, you might not notice that the pitch attitude has changed, that the VSI is pointing upward and that the altimeter is beginning to wind clockwise. You might also assume that you are watching those instruments, but your mind is elsewhere, registering readings according to your desires and perhaps your frustrations regarding aircraft heading.

As fatigue, boredom and complacency set in, it becomes more likely that unnoticed control-induced deviations will occur and continue to be overlooked by an inefficient scan.

Even with an airplane in perfect trim, over time, the discipline of pilot steadiness may falter. Without realizing it, you press the yoke or a pedal a bit harder. You may release tensions through muscular response just enough to get the airplane climbing or turning. Again, steady flying is a continuous process of minor adjustments made in response to continuously monitored instrument indications.

We usually can't feel ourselves exerting unwanted control pressures, especially when we're tired. In executing a difficult maneuver or in handling even a minor crisis, like trying to find a pencil as a clearance flows in from ATC, at least a small amount of tension is bound to be transmitted through our limbs to the controls. Trying to avoid all such pressure inputs is like trying constantly to regulate breathing.(Many pilots compound this problem by failing to trim properly. They try to use the trim to set altitude via the VSI, which won't work.)

It's far better to regulate and dampen the effects of inadvertent control inputs by countering them as soon as their effects appear. If you affect the yoke, the AI will show it, followed closely by the VSI, airspeed indicator and altimeter. If you express tension with a heavy left foot, the tendency of the left wing to drop will be evidenced on the attitude indicator. By catching that indication and correcting for it immediately, you can prevent the turning tendency that your heading indicator would soon show.

The best way to monitor how level your wings are is not to rely on the wings that grace the middle of the attitude indicator but the pointer at the top, which indicates the angle of bank. The pointer makes that easier to determine than do the wings at the artificial horizon.

The ability to dampen out unwanted control inputs is one of the greatest advantages of an efficient scan. During climbing and turning

maneuvers, it is easy to translate your concentration on precise execution of that maneuver into forgetfulness about what else the airplane is
doing. To avoid assuming unusual or, more likely, unwanted attitudes,
consult the AI whenever you change the pitch or bank. The power
indicator is, of course, your direct power control. These gauges set
attitude and power.

The performance that control produces is indicated by the airspeed
indicator, altimeter, vertical speed indicator, heading indicator and
turn coordinator (or indicator).

The AI is the keypoint of the scan, yet some pilots tend to omit this
instrument. One reason may be impatience to see the results on the
other instruments of the initiated changes. As you move your scan from
gauge to gauge, keep returning to the AI. Otherwise, you may end up
only chasing the performance needles.

Common Faults

Some other frequent errors:

• Fixating on the power indicator when a power change is made. Set the
power, note the setting, continue scanning, return to the power indicator in your next sweep and reset as necessary.
• Changing pitch with trim. Instead, set the pitch with the yoke, using
the AI for positioning data and the airspeed indicator to determine the
airspeed the pitch obtains. Then trim to set the yoke at the position.
• Omitting the AI in controlling heading. Keep the wings level with the
top pointer of the AI and monitor the heading through the heading
indicator.
• Make all pitch changes with the AI. Note the VSI, altimeter and
airspeed indicator for resultant climb/descent or airspeed.
• During speed changes, failure to keep the VSI and altimeter in the
scan, resulting in unwanted descents or climbs.
• Neglecting the AI, and thus pitch changes, when the power is
changed.
• Failure to check the AI's nose dot against pitch changes in level turns.
• Fixating on the HI in rolling out of a turn. Refer frequently to the
attitude indicator for bank angle while glancing at the DG for heading
purposes.
• Overbanking due to neglect of the turn coordinator and AI. Always
turn at precise bank angles.
• Fixating on an instrument but not fully reading it. For instance, in a
turn, noting the bank angle but ignoring a rising or falling nose dot.

In this section, we have not emphasized detailed scan patterns for specific maneuvers. Our intention has been to clarify how principles of scanning are violated and how you can guard against such errors. Hopefully, you will avoid the situation encountered by the 747 captain.

At the core is keeping focused on the whole airplane and therefore the whole panel. Alert scanning and registering of the gauges' messages is essentially a process of interrogation and response. Is the gauge saying what it should be saying? If not, what and how much adjustment (control) of power and/or attitude will effect the desired performance?

The instruments pose the questions and provide the answers. All it takes is the pilot's quick eyes and mind to bring maturity and civility to those mischievous needles.

Now let's take a closer look at some scanning particulars.

Scanning and Cross Checking

Many instrument pilots ask me during refresher training for ideas about cross-checking the gauges. It seems as if everyone is looking for the ultimate system to accomplish this. This is a tough question and we will share our beliefs about instrument scan/cross-check.

Not many long-time instrument pilots can explain how they do it except to say that they mare sure every instrument is scanned left to right and up and down with rapid eye movement. We constantly emphasize that in order to fly instruments safely and efficiently, you must be shifty-eyed. Fixating or omitting any one instrument or group of instruments can be deadly. A roving eye is said by some people to apply in certain social situations. The instrument pilot must indeed have a roving eye in the cockpit to ensure survival.

The Fundamentals

Whatever system you use for scanning can only be successful if you first have a thorough understanding of:

• how each instrument functions;
• what each instrument is telling you;
• how to analyze what is happening;
• how to verify what one instrument or group of instruments is telling you needs to be done; and
• what control responses are needed.

Once you have this understanding, it must be constantly reinforced by practice and rereading the basic instrument doctrine used during primary instrument training. Practice helps you keep the speed up of your roving eyes in order to give proper attention to each instrument and keep the airplane right side up.

Automatic Reaction

We act and react like Pavlov's dog. Some of you might remember from Psychology 101 that Pavlov found his dog could be stimulated to react with the same involuntary responses. For instrument pilots, the stimuli are the instrument readings and the reactions are the required control responses. Control responses must be accomplished simultaneously when called for by the specific maneuver and without conscious thought. For example, when in a diving spiral, you should first roll the wings level, reduce power and raise the nose as simultaneously as possible.

Ground Rules

We want to review some ground rules before continuing with a discussion of instrument stimuli and control response. The rules listed below weren't developed from personal opinion, but are described extensively in the FAA Instrument Flight Training Handbook, AC 61-27C.

• When power is variable, power controls airspeed.
• The primary bank instrument for straight and level, climbs and descents on a heading is the heading indicator.

Primary is the most pertinent, essential instrument for the maneuver in question, but not necessarily the only one. The airplane won't turn unless it's banked. Whenever you see the HI move, verify the bank with the attitude indicator (AI) and turn coordinator. Correct the bank with a control input. Some critics might say you can turn the airplane by skidding or slipping, but these aren't turns and should never be considered as turns.

• The primary pitch instrument for maintaining altitude is the altimeter.

We know that the VSI is a pitch instrument also, which indicates a trend before the altimeter indicates a climb or descent. While both instruments have some lag, the VSI has less lag than the altimeter. Responding to the VSI allows you to make a control response before the altimeter indicates a climb or descent. This is why it's usually easier to hold altitude during steep turns by reacting to VSI changes. If you wait for the altimeter to change, it's usually too late to avoid large altitude deviations.

• The turn coordinator (TC) is primary for establishing and maintaining a standard rate turn. The AI is used to first set the bank, which is fine-tuned by the TC.
• The glideslope indicator is primary for pitch during an ILS approach.

How It Works

Let's apply these rules for an ILS approach. When entering a level turn, the airspeed will decay as you adjust the pitch to maintain altitude. The appropriate response is to add power when entering the turn. The response to any airspeed change while trying to maintain a constant altitude or pitch is a power adjustment, assuming power is variable.

When on the glideslope, you must maintain a pitch attitude that ensures arrival at decision height with the glideslope indicator centered and the airspeed controlled with power. This technique results in easier cross-checking and smoother approaches. If you have any doubts, watch an autopilot during a coupled ILS approach. It maintains the glideslope with pitch and you must control airspeed with the throttle(s).

Once you fully understand the instruments, their functions and the control responses needed, you'll have an acute awareness that scanning techniques and emphasis aren't static. They must be adjusted depending on the maneuvers to be accomplished. For example, the same cross-check emphasis for a steep turn won't work for an ILS approach.

As you intercept the localizer, more emphasis must be placed on the localizer and glideslope indicators. We say both indicators because you'd be surprised how many non-current instrument pilots get so intent on intercepting and maintaining the localizer that they fail to respond to the glideslope. This is also often the case with an HSI.

CDI Cross-Check

It's necessary to refer to the CDI more than usual to detect and react to the slightest movement of the two indicators. You must deliberately pick up the CDI in your cross-check and then return to the altimeter, airspeed, attitude indicator, etc. If you don't do this, you'll suddenly find the indicators going off-scale, requiring large corrections and increased workload to restore your position.

During a front course approach, as soon as you detect the CDI moving off center, you must immediately turn toward the indicator. A half-standard rate turn should be sufficient unless the indicator is moving rapidly off-center or off-scale, in which case a normal standard rate turn might be needed.

Plan to roll out just before the CDI re-centers. While you don't want to eliminate the HI from your scan, it's less important at this point than the CDI. You can hold the inbound course by paying more attention and reacting to the localizer indicator than consciously seeking a constant heading that will take you down the slot. It's unusual to have such steady winds that a single heading at the start of the approach will be the same heading upon arrival at DH.

Since you devote more attention to the CDI, you have a better opportunity to pick up the glideslope intercept. At this point, the gear and approach flaps (if required) should be extended and the power reduced to maintain approach airspeed. You might find that in your quest to center the localizer that you failed to notice the glideslope indicator either moving off center or coming into view.

You need to develop the understanding that pitch and trim control responses must be as rapid as your response to the localizer indicator excursions from center. Corrections should be small at the outset and you should resist the tendency (when one or two dots low on the glideslope) of pulling up to re-intercept.

Re-Intercepting The Glideslope

The proper way to re-intercept is to level off and add power to maintain airspeed until the needle returns to center. When approaching glideslope centerline, you should reestablish your rate of descent, reduce power to your target airspeed and hold the glideslope on center with pitch and trim. Remember, power controls airspeed, not the glideslope. While it's important to cross-check the airspeed during descent, it's far more critical to keep the localizer and glideslope indicators centered and you'll find it's much less workload to use pitch rather than power to control the descent.

Cover the HI

If you experience difficulty keeping the localizer centered due to cross-check problems, try covering the HI and work one of the partial panel procedures that was described earlier in the book. If you practice this procedure, you'll either pick up the CDI in your cross-check or you won't find the runway. Besides, it's good practice for improving partial panel work.

As soon as we notice that someone isn't cross-checking the turn coordinator or needle/ball, we cover the attitude indicator for a while and the cross-check soon improves remarkably. Many times after a four to six hour refresher session, pilots have sometimes remarked that when the AI was uncovered, they weren't uncomfortable without it and didn't need it.

Scanning Proficiency Program

Here are our recommendations for developing a good cross-check program:

1. Refresh yourself on the instruments and their individual functions.
2. Review the maneuvers and the primary instruments for each.
3. Practice scan techniques that help you to sweep the panel.
4. Practice partial panel VOR and ILS approaches periodically.
5. Never look away from the instruments for more than a second or two.
6. Schedule some simulator time monthly to help sharpen your scan.

Aircraft Handling

T his chapter is devoted to a variety of topics related to handling your aircraft properly while flying IFR.

To begin with, we'll present two specific programs of exercises to help you keep your instrument flying skill sharp.

A Proficiency Primer

Time for an instrument flying review. What follows is an advanced syllabus aimed at pilots who are already instrument-rated. Although this is designed as a do-it-yourself kit, you'll need a safety pilot from time-to-time.

All the practice work here should first be accomplished VFR without using a hood. Doing this will speed your instrument interpretation relative to aircraft attitude. A bit of mystery is removed when you compare instrument indications to outside references, thus rebuilding confidence.

Always work for maximum precision when practicing the maneuvers. Don't proceed to the next maneuver until you've mastered the recommended goals. Your precision should exceed the requirements for the FAA Instrument Practical Test Standards. We think our readers are better than that and will agree that an ILS approach that varies from one to four dots deflection is unacceptable performance.

Pitch & Power
Attitude Indicator:

1. Fly straight and level and adjust the horizon bar. Hold altitude with the attitude indicator only and cross-check the altimeter.
2. Keep the wings level and don't worry about heading yet.
3. Maintain a constant airspeed with changes in power. Keep these changes as small and smooth as possible.
4. Change airspeed at least 10 knots with power while maintaining altitude with altimeter and VSI. The horizon bar moves up on deceleration, down on acceleration.
5. Initiate one-half and one horizon bar climbs/descents and cross-check for VSI rates. Note and record power settings for 300 and 500 fpm climb/descent. Select and maintain a constant airspeed with power if power is available.

Concentration:

1. Smooth air performance goals:
 +/- 50 feet and 5 knots.
2. Cross-check attitude indicator, altimeter, VSI and airspeed indicator.
3. Smooth control responses - no movement, just pressure.
4. Make small corrections, avoid over controlling.
5. Observe visual attitude of aircraft compared to attitude indicator.
6. Trim for control when changing pitch and power.

Altimeter and VSI:

1. Practice pitch changes using the altimeter as primary and observe the horizon bar on attitude indicator.
2. Notice that, after making a pitch change, the VSI moves before the altimeter. The VSI is a trend instrument and warns that the altimeter is about to change.
The altimeter and VSI are barometric instruments which lag. The altimeter lags more than the VSI, but if smooth pitch changes are made, the lag is not apparent. If the aircraft has an instantaneous VSI (IVSI), there is no apparent lag and you can react to pitch changes before the altimeter moves.

Concentration:

1. Performance goals: +/- 50 feet and +/- 5 knots.
2. Practice holding altitude with the VSI exclusively. React to needle movement instantly. Control changes should be made with pressure not movement.

3. Observe altimeter lag before it reacts to pitch changes.
4. Make pitch changes with AI and observe VSI reacting before altimeter.
5. Hold altitude with altimeter while cross-checking attitude indicator and VSI. When observing VSI trends, relax or increase back pressure in small increments until desired performance is obtained.
6. Remember to trim.

Airspeed indicator:

1. When power is variable, power controls airspeed.
2. The airspeed indicator is a pitch instrument when there is no power, full power or when you choose not to change or cannot change power.
3. Airspeed is primary for pitch when climbing or descending at a constant airspeed.
4. When climbing or descending at constant rates, airspeed is primary for power, if power is variable. If power is not variable and you want to change airspeed, then a pitch change is necessary and you accept whatever rate of climb or descent results.
5. Practice holding airspeed using the airspeed indicator only.
6. Use all pitch instruments to maintain airspeed.
7. Use power to change airspeed 15-20 knots and maintain altitude using all available instruments.
8. Remember to trim.

Concentration:

1. Small control movements with pressure only. Always trim to relieve pressure.
2. Cross-check must be more rapid due to altitude changes and additional instruments added to scan.
3. Goals: +/- 50 feet and +/- 5 knots.

Bank Control

The heading indicator is primary for bank control in straight and level flight. The attitude indicator and turn coordinator are supporting in this situation.

The turn coordinator indicates a standard rate turn and a bank in either direction. I have noticed that many pilots use rudder to displace the miniature airplane or needle on this instrument and place the airplane in a slip or skid. Remember, the rudder controls the ball and the ailerons are used for bank. Concentrate on smoothly coordinating the use of both.

When establishing a standard rate turn, set the approximate bank angle with the attitude indicator, then use the turn coordinator to adjust the bank to maintain a standard rate turn. The turn coordinator is primary for bank once the turn is established.

Now that you have reviewed pitch, power and bank, you're ready to integrate the three into exercises. Practice without the hood first and complete each exercise using full and partial panel. Your performance goals should be +/- 50 feet, +/- 5 knots and +/- 3 degrees.

Climbs and Descents
Constant airspeed climbs and descents:

1. Change from cruise to climb/descent power while maintaining altitude.
2. Use the airspeed indicator as primary pitch and maintain a constant airspeed.
3. Climb/descend and level-off at predetermined altitudes, then change to cruise airspeed. Control airspeed with power.
4. During climbs and descents with full panel, perform standard rate turns to predetermined headings and timed turns with a partial panel.

Constant rate climbs and descents:

1. From cruise airspeed, change to climb/descent airspeed while maintaining altitude.
2. Climb/descend using the VSI for primary pitch. Level-off at predetermined altitudes changing primary pitch control to the altimeter. Control airspeed with power.
3. During climbs and descents with full panel, perform standard rate turns to predetermined headings and timed turns when partial panel.

Turns
Standard rate timed turns:

1. The turn coordinator or needle/ball must be calibrated before proceeding. Establish a standard rate turn and determine the amount of needle deflection to hold a 3-degree per second turn.
2. Practice 45-, 90-, 180-, 270- and 360-degree turns with constant airspeed and altitude.
3. Practice 180, 270 and 360 timed turns while changing airspeed 10-5 knots at constant altitude.

4. Make sure control responses entering and rolling out of the turns are the same.

5. Practice changing airspeed as turn entry is commenced.

Magnetic compass turns:

1. Practice partial panel turns from north to south and south to north using the magnetic compass only.

Remember, when turning north, undershoot by the latitude plus half the bank angle. When turning to south, overshoot by the latitude minus the bank angle. For headings of east and west, no overshoot or under-shoot is required except to allow for the bank angle.

ANDS is the best way to remember Acceleration North, Deceleration South. At a stabilized airspeed and altitude, while on a heading of east or west, reduce power, hold altitude and notice that the compass turns toward south. Reapply power and notice a turn toward north.

2. Head east or west at stabilized airspeed and altitude. Reduce power and hold altitude. Notice how the compass indicates a turn toward south. As you apply power, notice a turn toward north.

Steep turns (VFR, full and partial panel):

1. Establish a 45-degree bank (+/- 5o) with full panel.

2. Enter a steep turn in one direction for 360 degrees, then roll into 360-degree steep turn in the opposite direction without pausing.

3. Control airspeed with available power.

4. Experience indicates that altitude is easier to maintain if the VSI is primary for pitch. Control responses must react to VSI trends by relaxing or adding back pressure. Once the altimeter winds down in a descent, it may be too late to hold altitude without shallowing bank angle.

This is where altimeter lag is a problem. The VSI has less lag and should warn when control response is required, before altitude loss or gain becomes significant.

5. When practicing steep turns partial panel, the turn coordinator or needle/ball is primary for bank.

Slow Flight and Stalls

Since these maneuvers are rarely practiced except in anticipation of a flight check, I have included some exercises that should emphasize how slow flight and approaches to stalls demand a good cross-check and control response. Don't forget to clear the area before conducting these maneuvers.

1. Configure the aircraft for 120 percent of the power-off stall speed with either or both landing gear and flaps extended.
2. Practice 180 and 360-degree standard rate turns in both directions while maintaining 120 percent of stall speed.
3. When straight and level, reduce power and maintain altitude until the aircraft just approaches the stall and recover. Altitude loss should be minimal.
4. Establish standard rate turns in both directions and reduce power, holding altitude until the aircraft approaches a stall. Recover to straight and level with minimal altitude loss.
5. It's preferable to hold altitude with reduced power until the aircraft approaches the stall rather than exerting back pressure to induce the stall. This improves your cross-check abilities and provides a realistic example of an inadvertent stall that could occur, for example, with a load of ice.

Unusual Attitudes

With a safety pilot or flight instructor, practice recovering from nose high, nose low and spiral situations with full and partial panel.

Most attitude indicators tumble at extreme pitch and bank angles. Consequently, it's important to control the aircraft by reference to the turn coordinator, VSI, airspeed indicator and altimeter (not necessarily in that order).

Nose low:

1. Increasing airspeed, nose low: reduce power.
2. Level wings and center ball with coordinated control response.
3. Altimeter winding down: apply back pressure smoothly to level flight. Adjust power.

Nose high:

1. Airspeed decaying, nose high: Increase power.
2. Level wings and center ball with coordinated response.
3. Apply forward pressure smoothly to level flight. Adjust power.

The primer we just presented can give you a real workout, but it's intended to be used on training flights only.

Here are some more exercises, specifically designed so that you can do them on every flight. This makes your flying time more valuable, in the sense that you're essentially accomplishing a training task while getting from Point A to Point B.

Ten Exercises for Proficiency

Few of us ever get enough practice at all the aspects of instrument flying. Under actual IFR conditions, the tendency is to complete the flight by the simplest means and "not make waves." Few of us ever request the full approach when we can get vectors.

The system was designed to get aircraft from here to there efficiently. A pilot who just wants to fly around in the clouds, or try some seldom-used approach, throws a wrench into the works. Under VFR conditions, most pilots ignore the tedious and time- consuming IFR system altogether.

Instrument competency checks become mini checkrides, with little if any actual learning taking place. It's little wonder that most of us have difficulty maintaining instrument flying proficiency.

There is something you can do on every flight to improve your instrument flying. And there are some exercises you can practice, with a safety pilot in the right seat and the hood pulled down over your eyes, to improve your performance in the clouds dramatically.

Precision Flying

Regardless of whether you're VFR or IFR, be as precise as possible. Never settle for good enough. For the instrument checkride, you must maintain altitude within 100 feet and maintain heading within 10 degrees. As soon as you can do this, you should maintain altitude within 50 feet and heading within five degrees. Then work on twenty-five feet and 2.5 degrees. The goal is to continue to refine this skill.

Likewise, when tracking the VOR, whether VFR or IFR, determine the exact heading that will track the airway and take you over the station. Remember, what you're looking for is an exact heading. If your heading varies more than five degrees, you're chasing the needle.

A Gentle Touch

When doing all this, steer the airplane with your finger tips. Use the rudder and trim so at any time you can let go of the controls without a significant pitch or roll change. Be very critical of your own performance. Believe it or not, the airplane can be flown with almost no control movement.

From time-to-time, see how quickly you can level-off from a climb, set the power, mixture and cowl flaps, and trim the airplane for absolute hands-off flight. This exercise will impress upon your subconscious mind the subtle trim changes that result from the aircraft accelerating from climb to cruise speed.

Controlled Descent

When approaching an airport on a VFR flight, pick an exact point to reduce the power to a predetermined setting and then leave it alone until the flare. For example, upon beginning your descent from cruising altitude, reduce power to 15 inches of manifold pressure. Then adjust the pitch of the aircraft to control rate of descent so that you arrive at traffic pattern altitude five miles from the airport. If you're flying a normally-aspirated airplane, it'll be necessary to adjust the throttle(s) to maintain 15 inches, but try to keep the power setting the same.

After you arrive at traffic pattern altitude, add pitch to slow the airplane while maintaining altitude. On downwind, lower the landing gear and approach flaps which should allow you to begin another descent. Use the flaps, adjust the pitch and size of the traffic pattern so that you cross the threshold with the engine(s) still at 15 inches. Not only will the exercise add hundreds of hours to the life of your engine(s), but it will build good habits for the future. There is, by the way, no guarantee that 15 inches is the magic number. You have to work that one out for your airplane.

IFR in VFR Conditions

Many of us tend to shy away from filing IFR in VFR conditions because of the delay in getting a clearance and IFR release. Remember though, if you file IFR in VFR conditions you're not obliged to get your clearance before takeoff. You can depart the airport VFR and then pick up your clearance en route. You lose some of the practice in doing this, but it's nice to know you have the option. When you call for your clearance, ask if there is any anticipated delay in departure. If there is, depart VFR. If not, copy the whole clearance and fly the departure procedure for practice.

There are several advantages to following an IFR clearance and flight plan in VFR conditions. Of course, the biggest benefit comes from increased familiarity with the ATC system. Beyond that, you develop a sense of reality which otherwise doesn't exist when you're in the clouds. Once you see what a 20-degree correction looks like when tracking the localizer, you'll never again use too much correction to center the needle.

Crosswind and Downwind Landings

Oftentimes the best approach course doesn't lead to the best runway. ILS approaches are often compromised because of terrain considerations. When the weather is below circling minima, you must make a straight-in approach to landing regardless of the wind. Hence VFR practice in this area can help a lot.

When flying an ILS approach to a downwind landing you'll frequently find yourself high and fast due to the tailwind on the approach. VFR practice allows you to develop alternative power settings which allow you to follow the glideslope downwind, and also help you develop the perceptual ability to quickly determine how much tailwind is too much for your airplane and your ability.

Crosswind landings are important too. Nothing is worse than making a perfect ILS approach only to flop down on the runway in a crab and then slide off the side of the active. Remember, runways at the bottom of an instrument approach are often wet. Dubious landing technique becomes dangerous landing technique when the runway gets slick. Develop the ability to land in a substantial crosswind and then track straight down the centerline of the runway with the upwind wheel planted firmly. If you are uncomfortable in cross winds, practice.

Circling Approaches

The VFR traffic pattern, with a 1000-foot downwind leg and a two-mile final, gives little practice for a circling approach under a 600-foot ceiling with a mile visibility. In order to fly these approaches in IMC, you must practice them in VFR.

When arriving at remote airports, fly a 600-foot, one-mile traffic pattern whenever possible. Announce your intentions on the CTAF and keep a sharp look-out for other traffic. The bigger and faster an airplane you fly, the larger your VFR traffic pattern is likely to be. Knowing what is required to execute a circling maneuver in your airplane could convince you to pass-up some approaches which otherwise look good on paper.

Fly By The Numbers

Whenever you're flying VFR, use fixed power settings which can be used in instrument flying. Find the exact power setting and configuration that allows you to track the glideslope, the amount of power required to level-off from a descent with the gear and flaps lowered, and exactly how much pitch should be used on a go-around to arrest the rate of descent. All these things are easy to ignore when VFR because we can gauge the values and results by looking out the windows. But if you can reduce the things to actual pitch and power indications on the instruments, you will be a step ahead when in the clouds.

Procedure Turns

Eventually though, you'll have to get a safety pilot and put on the hood to hone your instrument skills. One of the best maneuvers to practice is the procedure turn. It can be practiced over any VOR or NDB, out of harm's way, without the distraction of having to cope with ATC.

When just a mile or two from the VOR, have your safety pilot pull an approach chart at random from the book. Then fly to the VOR and execute the procedure turn. Remember, you want to do this with a light touch, a minimum of maneuvering and using fixed power settings. Strive for perfection.

Fly a two-minute outbound leg, the published procedure turn, and on the inbound leg, have your safety pilot give you another one. If you blow it, go back to the VOR and try again. Once you get to where you can handle these with minimal heading or altitude excursions, try this: On the outbound leg, slow the airplane to approach speed and lower the gear and approach flaps. On the inbound leg, clean the airplane up and go back to cruise speed.

Another good exercise is to fly procedure turns without a chart. Pick a radial and track it outbound. When it's time to execute the turn, make a 45-degree turn to the right or left. After one minute, make a 180-degree turn in the opposite direction from which you made the first turn. Intercept the original radial and track it inbound. Practice these for a few times and you'll never again get lost in the middle of the process.

Holding Patterns

Few of us ever get sufficient opportunity to practice holding patterns. Once again, they can be practiced at any VOR or NDB without ATC interference. When approaching the fix, have your safety pilot pick a number between zero and 360 and a direction of right or left. If your safety pilot chooses 165 and left, for example, use that for your holding clearance. You are to hold on the 165 degree radial or bearing, in left turns.

These exercises aren't designed to see if you can do it perfectly, they are designed so that you can make mistakes, in relative safety, and thereby learn. Just fly to the fix and try to get into the holding pattern anyway you can. If, after several tries, you can't make the thing work, take off the hood and watch what's happening in relationship to the VOR. If there's a strong wind, try a few crosswind and with the wind.

Remember, it's supposed to be a learning experience.

Once you have a handle on holds at the station, try a few at intersections. Throughout the exercise, constantly remind your safety pilot to keep a sharp look out. Over VORs and on airways there is an increased likelihood of encountering traffic. Also, it's easy for the safety pilot to get fascinated by what's going on in the cockpit.

ADF Practice

There's no better way to improve your ADF technique than to practice procedure turns and holding patterns over a radio station. Unlike VOR practice, if you use a broadcast station you won't be on an intersection or over a primary navigation fix. Once again, remember these things are practice. The goal is to increase your knowledge and skill, not to do it right the first time.

Try several procedure turns and holding patterns. If they don't work out, take off the hood and do them while watching the station. Watch what the airplane does, relative to the station, and what the ADF needle does. You can learn more in one hour with this type of practice than you can in a week's worth of classroom study.

Notice in the previous exercise that little mention was made about instrument approaches. That's because of all procedures, approaches are what we tend to get the most practice on. For most of us, practice involves donning the hood and flying a few approaches. Often the approaches are the same ones we have been flying for years.

It All Comes Together

The instrument approach is really the culmination of the instrument flight. If you can fly on instruments; if you can fly procedure turns and holding patterns like the airplane was on railroad tracks; if you know exactly what power and pitch settings will produce the desired performance; if you can maneuver the airplane in tight places and land gently and accurately, regardless of wind; then flying the approach itself is simple.

By spending a few hours practicing these maneuvers in a non-threatening environment, you can greatly increase you instrument flying skills for a minimum investment in gasoline, perspiration and adrenalin. Let's face it, we can all use the practice.

Now that we've got you jumping through hoops, stop for a moment and give some thought to how you're handling the airplane. Are you driving it around the sky as if it were a school bus?

If you can develop a little finesse and technique, you'll find that your flights go smoother, are less fatiguing, and kinder to your passengers to boot. Here's how.

The Egg In Hand Routine

An airplane doesn't know whether you're operating VFR or IFR. It flies exactly the same in and out of the clouds, so any difference in the precision with which it is flown is strictly due to pilot technique.

There's a world of difference, however, between controlling an airplane when you can see the ground and when you can't. Unfortunately, many pilots, in spite of learning that instrument flying is more difficult, decide they have what it takes to fly in the soup without the proper training. They usually don't get very far.

Imagine you're a VFR pilot again, flying in the clouds for the first time and having difficulty. When you had the whole world in front of you, you looked out the window and flew the airplane in reference to the horizon for a particular maneuver. You occasionally glanced at the altimeter to maintain altitude and possibly the heading indicator to verify the outside view. Why did you have difficulty doing the same thing when the world wasn't visible?

Having The Big Picture

The answer lies in what we call the big picture. When flying in VMC, the brain receives most of its information from one source. If the earth is retreating, you're climbing. In a turn, the airplane is banked and your eyes relay to the brain that the wing is at a given angle, and the airplane is turning around its longitudinal axis.

In the clouds, however, there are several sources of information about the airplane's flight condition. All the flight instruments must be scanned simultaneously and the information each instrument provides must be seen by the eyes, absorbed by the brain and the big picture of the airplane's performance must be developed. All this takes time.

The inexperienced instrument pilot, who has yet to develop good scan technique, usually focuses too long on each instrument and tries to correct a problem on one instrument before moving on to the next. Instead of developing an understanding of what is happening to the airplane, he/she tries to force each instrument to read the way he/she wants it to, one at a time. This technique is not conducive to longevity in the clouds.

The Death-Grip Method

There are several problems with this situation. First, the pilot usually has a death-grip on the controls, holding on so tight that he/she gets little feedback or feeling from the controls. The second problem is anxiety, which builds whether the pilot is in the clouds or under the hood with an instructor. This tenses the body and the pilot feels airplane movements even less. He/she fixates on one instrument, to the point where nothing makes sense anymore. Hopefully, the instructor is savvy enough to understand the situation and helps the pilot out of this self-induced quandary.

To fly basic instruments properly requires experience, relaxation and confidence. Not over-confidence in your abilities, but the knowledge that your training allows you to properly employ your skills as needed.

Developing the proper skills takes time. Even after getting the instrument rating, your skills will mature provided you put forth the effort required. This can lead to other problems. For example, many instrument pilots who aren't current and proficient expect to operate IFR and still fly competently. It doesn't work that way.

A friend recently asked me to ride as safety pilot while he went out to work on his currency. It had been many months since he had last flown on the gauges, and his performance was typical. He manhandled the airplane, as his scan was too slow to keep up with the airplane. He couldn't have passed an instrument checkride to save his life that day.

Over-Controlling

Many instrument and non-instrument pilots can't understand that over-controlling the airplane will get you into trouble, especially in the clouds. Pilots who can't relax when on the gauges tend to over-correct for everything. For example, a simple heading change of five degrees is accomplished with a 20-degree bank, overshooting the desired heading, and then using the same bank angle in the opposite direction to correct back. After several bank oscillations, the pilot finally establishes the desired heading.

In the meantime, while fixating on the heading indicator, the airplane is descending at 500 feet per minute. When the pilot finally scans the altimeter or VSI and discovers the descent, he/she will usually do a panic-pull on the controls and a 1500 fpm climb will results. He/she will overshoot the target altitude and go through a series of vertical oscillations until the altitude is squared away. Then, the pilot will catch something else amiss and start the whole scenario over.

While your primary source of information comes from the gauges, you must still rely to a certain degree on the feel of the airplane and how it responds to control inputs and to atmospheric conditions. A relaxed, confident instrument pilot feels what the airplane is doing through the controls before or as the information becomes available on the gauges. We can't emphasize strongly enough that control-feel alone isn't enough to fly the airplane without instruments. We're all familiar with the problems of spatial disorientation.

How do professional instrument pilots get the airplane to slide down the glideslope with the needles cemented in place regardless of the conditions? First, pilots who fly a lot usually stay current and proficient. The more flying you do, the better prepared you are to face more complex tasks and handle them routinely. The ability to scan the instruments quickly and get the big picture is the first step toward competent instrument flying.

Next is the way the pilot handles the controls. Over-controlling requires an increased scan rate to keep up with the induced oscillations. However, most pilots over control because they can't scan fast enough.

The Egg-In-Hand Method

There's a simple and effective way to learn how to fly smoothly on the gauges: the Egg In Hand Routine. Start with the premise that from the moment you roll down the runway until you taxi at the end of the flight, there's a raw egg between the palm of your hand and the control wheel.

This exercise has several advantages. First, you can't develop a death-grip on the controls that eliminates feedback. You must hold the controls with only your fingertips. Holding the controls in this manner is the beginning of good instrument flying.

Second, with the threat of breaking the egg always present, and the mess that would result, you'll smoothly and gently control the airplane. You'll have more time to scan the instruments during a maneuver is in progress, as you'll maintain a normal scan rate, instead of increasing it as when you were over- controlling.

This routine seems difficult at first, because your scan will move at a faster than is necessary. At the same time, you'll be hesitant to react out of fear of having egg in your lap and in the airplane.

While it's necessary to quickly scan all the instruments to get the big picture, when you over control, a conflict within the brain develops. It works faster, but doesn't have time to interpret all the information. In this situation, you never get the big picture and you only react to the instrument on which you're fixating, thereby slowing the whole process. The brain has more time to interpret each instrument and understand the big picture.

It Becomes Automatic

As we said in the beginning, there's no physical difference between flying the airplane in the clouds versus VFR conditions. For example, in good visibility, you seldom think about what's necessary to enter a 30-degree bank. Like driving a car, you execute the maneuver based on a preconceived picture of how it should look.

Why should it be any different when you're in the clouds? It wouldn't be if you flew IFR as much as you fly VFR, which brings us back to the question of currency versus proficiency.

Using the egg-in-hand routine will help you become a more proficient pilot. You'll understand that there's no difference flying a 30-degree bank whether you're on the gauges or VFR. It will eliminate the need to rush to correct a deficiency observed on one gauge until you've coordinated it with the big picture.

The next time you fly, keep track of the number of eggs you break. As you progress, there will be fewer and fewer.

Try It VFR First

When you're VFR, watch the instruments and the rate at which they change while entering a turn, climb or descent. Then, try the death-grip method of control while under the hood. You'll find the instruments react much faster than when you're VFR. Why? Because you're rushing to complete the maneuver, using only one or two instruments instead of developing the picture used when VFR. Then try the egg-in-hand routine. You'll notice a change for the better as you slow the action and have time to understand the big picture.

As you continue the routine, you'll develop better scan technique, since you'll have more time to scan. You'll feel better about your instrument flying because you'll be a better instrument pilot. Once you get yourself up to speed with this routine, maintain your proficiency with a safety pilot to keep you instrument flying smooth and proficient.

Once established in some sort of steady-state flight, say straight-and-level cruise, a standard rate turn, a climb, or a descent, most instrument pilots can do a pretty good job of controlling the airplane.

Real skill shows, however, during the transitions from one state to another. One of the toughest is nailing down a target altitude. All too often, we see students overshoot their assigned altitude, and then spend an inordinate amount of time chasing it. Here are some tips on nailing down the shift to level flight.

Transitioning to Level Flight

We've often heard instrument flying described as if it were a juggling act. You have to keep all the balls in the air, the instrument flight instructor tells the student. Instructors often describe the introduction of a new maneuver as tossing in another ball.

If you watch good instrument pilots—the old masters—they hardly look like they're juggling. In fact, the better an instrument pilot is, the less he or she moves. As a flight instructor, when giving instrument competency checks or refresher training it's easy to spot the jugglers. They're busy. And because their ability to fly an airplane depends upon the skill of juggling, that skill soon fades if it isn't practiced regularly. With the jugglers, all that's necessary to throw the whole program off the track is to give them one too many balls, which as any pilot knows, is pretty easy to do.

Transition To Cruise

Where the business of instrument flight juggling breaks down is during the transition to level flight. In a climb, pitch can take care of itself. If the airplane is trimmed at anything less than cruise airspeed, and if climb power is set, the airplane will climb. The pitch might fluctuate five or ten degrees and this is certainly sloppy flying. But the end result will always be a climb.

As the airplane nears its assigned altitude, you must become aware of pitch. The pitch must be adjusted to allow the airplane to accelerate toward cruise airspeed. So add one ball. Because you haven't been making pitch adjustments in the climb, the addition of control pressure will almost always cause you to add a slight amount of aileron so suddenly roll control becomes more difficult.

As the airplane accelerates, torque and P-factor change, which requires rudder inputs. Now heading and coordination control become more demanding so this adds another couple of balls to the juggling act. During the process, cruise power must be set, the cowl flaps closed and the mixture leaned.

It's a fact of life that Murphy's Law (that which can go wrong will go wrong) is an essential element of instrument flying. So you can bet if you must intercept an airway, change communications frequencies or copy an amended clearance, it will happen right in the middle of the transition to level flight. By now the juggler will be getting frantic.

The key element to removing the juggling from this important phase of a flight is to realize that if you're juggling, you're doing something wrong. If you barely have enough time to get from one maneuver to the next, you need to examine the fundamentals of your instrument flying technique.

How Long Does It Take?

Here's a test question. How long does it take the average student pilot to put an airplane into straight-and-level flight? The surprising answer is about 35 hours. Which isn't to say the student can't hold heading or altitude before that. Most student pilots can hold heading or altitude after ten hours of instruction.

The pilot can climb to cruise altitude and level off. But if you observe what is happening with the airplane, you'll notice it isn't in straight-and-level flight at all. In fact the airplane is constantly climbing above the altitude and then descending below. Rather than holding heading, the airplane is doing very slow and shallow Dutch rolls across a heading. The pilot is juggling and keeping all the balls in the air. But as soon as he/she stops scanning the instruments or the horizon to look at the chart, the airplane will go off heading and off altitude.

It usually takes a student 35 hours before getting an airplane into straight and level flight for the first time. Straight-and-level flight is where the airplane just roars along and you sit back and watch. If you look at a chart, when you look back up, the airplane is still on the desired heading and altitude. When an airplane is in straight-and-level flight, it will remain so unless acted upon by other forces.

Novice Vs Experience

Many instrument pilots have similar experiences. The reason straight and level flight seems so demanding is because what most inexperienced instrument pilots are doing isn't straight and level flight. What most novice pilots are doing is making Dutch rolls across and heading, and vertical S patterns across the assigned altitude. No wonder it seems like juggling.

The reason instrument flying is so much easier for experienced instrument pilots is because they put the airplane into the desired attitude and then leave it there. Let us restate this most important premise. The very good instrument pilots aren't better at juggling. They don't juggle.

In order to undo the tendency to juggle, it's necessary to relearn some things that have been with you since student pilot days. You have to forget about juggling and begin to understand the tendencies of your aircraft. You need to understand the airplane has certain characteristics and most of the juggling you do is just fighting against those characteristics. You need to constantly search for flight control equilibrium and if you're carrying control pressure, you're doing something wrong.

If You Don't Retrim

For example, suppose you're in straight and level flight and notice you're 200 feet low on the altimeter. If you're a juggler, you'll add back pressure, climb back to your assigned altitude and relax back pressure. But guess what. The next time you look at the altimeter, you'll be 200 feet low again. When you added back pressure to climb, you slowed the airplane slightly. When the airplane arrived at the assigned altitude and when you relaxed back pressure, the airplane wanted to return to cruise airspeed so in order to do it the nose dropped slightly to accelerate.

What would the old-master do if he/she was 200 feet low? Most likely, trim the airplane for 20 fpm climb and make a mental note to check back in 10 minutes. If in a big hurry to get back to altitude, he/she might trim the airplane into a 100 fpm climb and check back in two minutes. As we're not as meticulous as most, we would try to trim the airplane into about a two fpm climb and then we'd know for the next 100 minutes—nearly two hours—we wouldn't worry about our altitude because we would know we were somewhere between 200 feet low and right on target.

Detecting Trends

In order to fly instruments well, you must deal with very small indications and very small trends. You need to understand the propensity for the airplane to remain stable as trimmed. Try this experiment sometime. Under VFR conditions take 10 minutes and get your airplane trimmed up until it's precisely level; no climb and no descent. Then with back pressure on the controls, raise the nose above the horizon and then let go of the controls. Use gentle rudder pressure to keep the wings level and watch what happens.

After you let go the airplane will continue up for a while, pitch over and start back down. It will go down for a while and go quite fast, but resist the temptation to touch the controls. Eventually the nose will come back up and the airplane will head skyward again. But you know what will happen? After three or four of these oscillations, most light airplanes will resume straight-and-level flight and will be at nearly the same altitude it started. So you tell me. Why should anyone juggle to maintain altitude within 100 feet when the airplane will do it by itself if properly trimmed?

Heading Control

The same thing is true for heading control. If the juggler notices the airplane is 10 degrees off heading, the juggler will bank the airplane at least 10 degrees (usually 20) to bring it back over to heading. The next time the juggler looks, the airplane will be off heading again because it has never been steady on heading. The old master on the other hand will bank the airplane about one degree or just shift feet slightly on the rudder pedals. It might take the airplane several minutes to get back to heading with so small a correction, but all that time it's within 10 degrees and getting closer.

Stop Juggling

So the essence of good instrument flight is to simply quit juggling. Learn the aerodynamic tendencies of the aircraft you fly and you'll quit fighting them. Learn how to make very tiny corrections and become very sensitive to the trends and changes in the trends.

It takes a student pilot 35 hours to get an airplane into straight-and-level flight for the first time. Most low-time instrument pilots never get an airplane into straight and level flight when in IMC, but they continue to juggle instead. We can put an airplane into straight and level flight in less than two minutes, IFR or VFR. Juggling isn't any easier for us than it is for you. But instrument flying might be easier, because we don't juggle.

Many modern airplanes fly most of the time just fine without using the rudder. It's important during climbout, of course, and when doing departure stalls, and it even comes in handy for the odd slip.

But during cruise and approach, many pilots don't pay it much attention at all. That's a mistake.

The fact is that the rudder is enormously useful during approaches, since it allows you to fine-tune your heading with a remarkable degree of accuracy. Here's how.

Using the Rudder

Probably your earliest recollection of flight training is trying to steer an airplane down the centerline of a taxiway with your feet. During the first attempt, you pushed the wrong pedal, pushed the correct pedal too hard or perhaps didn't push hard enough. Just when you got the airplane under control, it headed for the weeds again.

We all shared this difficulty as neophyte pilots because early in life most of us learned to steer with our hands, whether the vehicle in question was a doll carriage or a Western Flyer red wagon. Learning to steer an airplane with our feet required a lot of relearning.

As a result of this difficulty, aircraft in the 1950s and 1960s were designed to be easier to steer with the feet. Of course, the most notable improvement was the tricycle landing gear with its ability to dampen an airplane's swerving tendencies. The goal of the aircraft designers was to minimize rudder pedal usage.

Many pilots don't realize that the rudder is really more important in flight than it is on the ground. The rudder is used to control adverse yaw generated by the engine, propeller and ailerons. Aircraft designers, in their quest to make an airplane drive like a car, went to great lengths to eliminate the need for rudder input by the pilot.

Look Ma, No Feet

The most dramatic example of this was the Aircoupe, which had no rudder pedals at all. The nosewheel steering was coupled to the control yoke. Rudder trim was added to the earliest Piper Cherokees so that the pilot could trim-out the effect of engine torque and P-factor in a climb. Even without the benefit of rudder trim, many pilots learned to climb in a slightly right- wing-low attitude to keep the airplane on heading.

In several airplane designs, the aileron cables were coupled to the rudder cables with springs so that the flat-footed pilot got a little rudder input whenever the ailerons were deflected. The most important breakthrough was differential ailerons; ailerons that traveled up more than they traveled down, creating much less adverse yaw.

As a result of these improvements, many pilots and some flight instructors don't have the unconscious habit of using the rudder to control the aircraft. During takeoff, they steer the airplane down the runway with their feet. As soon as the airplane stabilizes in a climb, they put their feet flat on the floor and drive the airplane through the sky.

Although these improperly-trained pilots can usually get the airplane from point A to point B, if the crosswind doesn't exceed the side-load capability of the landing gear, they've never developed the instinctive ability to control yaw with the rudder pedals. In turbulence, particularly in aircraft with poor stability around the normal axis (such as the V-tail Bonanza and most light twins), the aircraft begins a side-to-side yaw oscillation that soon results in the back-seat passengers getting a second view of their lunch in the bottom of a plastic bag.

This lack of training is particularly dangerous for multi-engine pilots, since when an engine quits at or near Vmc, the airplane yaws violently and the almost immediate result of this yaw is a roll. If the pilot cannot instinctively deal with the yaw, he or she will crank in full aileron to stop the roll. Disaster soon follows.

Flat-Footed Means More Work

For the instrument pilot who is accustomed to flying with feet flat on the floor, or without rudder input, holding a heading and making small heading corrections is extremely difficult. The reason for this is that the wings of the aircraft are almost never level. It takes the flat-footed pilot ten times as much time, energy and concentration to keep the airplane on course and heading.

To turn, you bank the aircraft and deflect the lift vector into the center of the turn, which pulls you around while you sit comfortably in the seat. To bank, you usually deflect the ailerons; the downward deflected aileron creates lift on one wing while the upward deflected aileron spills lift off the other.

Although differential ailerons go a long way to reduce adverse yaw, they still generate some and the greater the aileron deflection, the more adverse yaw generated. In other words, when you bank to the left, the nose of the aircraft moves to the right until the aircraft begins turning. The faster you roll into the bank, the further the nose of the aircraft will deflect in the opposite direction. This is why your flight instructor told you to apply rudder and aileron together.

Holding Heading

Let's apply this to the skill of holding a heading in instrument conditions. Imagine that you're tracking a localizer on an approach at 120 knots. You look down at the approach chart for a few moments to get the DH and to review the missed approach procedure. When you look up, the aircraft is nine degrees off your desired heading and banked to the right. Your reference heading was 270 so the aircraft is now on a heading of 279. The CDI is moving, so you want to get back on heading as quickly as possible.

If you're flying with your feet flat on the floor, or if your feet are resting uselessly on the rudder pedals, the first thing you'll do is use the ailerons to bank the aircraft to the left. Although the rule of thumb is to only use a bank angle half the amount of change desired, you're in a hurry to get back on heading, so you bank ten degrees. It takes two seconds to bank the airplane and because you haven't used rudder to correct for adverse yaw, the nose of the aircraft has moved three degrees further to the right, so the true aircraft heading when you arrive at ten degrees of left bank is now 282.

Ten degrees of bank gives about a half-standard rate turn at 120 knots. You have 12 degrees to turn at 1.5 degrees per second so it will take you another eight agonizing seconds to get back on heading, a total of ten seconds for the correction.

Stop reading for a moment and count ten seconds. It's a long time when an airplane is off course and the CDI is moving toward the peg. Under these circumstances, many pilots bank much further, to 20 or 30 degrees to correct a nine degree error. This scenario is the beginning of an S-turns across the localizer approach.

Now let's review another method of heading control. Instead of banking the airplane, stomp on the rudder and shove the nose of the aircraft over nine degrees. It can be done in one second instead of eight. Although this is an artificial turn because the airplane is actually skidding and traveling sideways on almost the same course as it was originally, the fuselage and that big vertical stabilizer aren't going to fly sideways for long and soon the airplane will streamline itself.

Beyond our ability to just shove the nose over to the desired heading with the rudder, when we apply rudder pressure, the airplane has a tendency to roll in the direction of the applied rudder.

Here is the absolute essence of easy heading control in instrument flight. Instead of using the ailerons for small heading changes, use the rudder. It's faster, easier and more accurate.

Ailerons Don't Cut It

If you use the ailerons to bank for a heading change, the heading won't change until the airplane is banked and after the adverse yaw is removed, a matter of seconds. If you use the rudder instead, the heading changes immediately, even before the airplane begins banking. In fact, it's the heading change that has caused the bank. You can easily hold heading to within one degree by keeping the wings level and using exquisite rudder inputs.

We learned this 20 years ago when we were flying a Beech 18 full of canceled bank checks into LAX. The weather was at absolute minimums and, fortunately for us, the chief pilot for the company was in the right seat, asleep. We flew the first approach and weaved our way down to near minimums rolling from side to side and trying to keep the needle in the donut. We missed the approach and the boss woke up when he heard the engines go to takeoff power. He let us try another approach, but we missed it again. After the second miss, when we planned on going to the alternate, he said, "Mind if I take a shot at it?"

Needless to say, we gave our permission.

Throughout the flight thus far, our boss had been reclining in the co-pilot seat, which was run to the lowest possible position, and all the way back. The top of his head was below the top of the instrument panel. To our surprise, he never straightened up. He just stuck his hands through the holes in the yoke, slid his feet onto the rudder pedals and looked bored.

From the time he intercepted the localizer, he never deflected the ailerons, not so much as a quarter of an inch. He simply left them alone and used the rudder to keep the airplane on heading. The heading never changed more than three degrees, the needles never moved from the center of the instrument, and we broke out over the exact centerline of the runway. It was the finest piece of instrument flying we ever saw and from that moment, we began making fine heading corrections with the rudder.

Rudder Proficiency

If, after sincere self examination, you find yourself lacking in the yaw control department, there are a few things you can do about it. The best method to learn rudder control is to take a course in aerobatics. When you can unconsciously roll an airplane around a point while using either hand on the stick, and when you can do super-slow rolls and point rolls, you'll know exactly what the rudder of an airplane does and when to use it. If you can't do this, much the same thing can be accomplished by practicing steep, violent Dutch rolls in a conventional airplane while holding the nose on a point on the horizon.

Whether you can take any additional primary training at all, you can improve rudder control on every flight. Never, absolutely never let the nose yaw from side to side in turbulence. Your rudder skills will improve and so will the digestion of your passengers.

Discipline yourself to control bank with rudder. If a small bank correction is required, level the wings with the rudder. If a small heading correction is required, make it with the rudder. You'll be surprised how well it works, how easy heading control becomes and how much time you have to do other things when you aren't S-turning down the localizer.

A pilot who can control heading within ten degrees is qualified for an instrument rating. The pilot who can hold heading exactly is an instrument pilot. There is a difference.

Time to shift gears a bit and talk about a specific kind of airplane: The twin.
Multi-engine airplanes deserve special mention because of their great handling demands on the pilot in the event of engine failure. Here are some tips from CFII John Conrad for you MEL pilots out there, intended to help improve your multi-engine proficiency.

Multi-Engine Proficiency

Many pilots fly twin-engine airplanes because they feel safer with two engines, but this can be a false sense of security. Although the rate in which accidents occur after an engine failure in light twins is less than half that of single-engine airplanes, an engine-failure accident in a light twin is almost twice as likely to be fatal.

A pilot's ability to safely land an airplane after an engine failure is a direct result of his or her proficiency. For example, a Cessna 340 and a Cessna Turbo 210 are powered by the same engine and will carry four people, baggage and four hours of fuel with IFR reserves. Both airplanes will carry six people if baggage and fuel are compromised.

When everything is normal, there isn't much more demand on the pilot of the C-340 than on the pilot of the C-T210. With five hours of training, a good T210 pilot can do an acceptable job of flying the C-340. However, during an emergency, there's a profound difference between the two airplanes.

I believe that an engine fire is the worst emergency you can encounter in IFR conditions. If it occurs in the T210, there isn't much to do except shut off the fuel, point the airplane toward the lowest terrain and hope you encounter VMC. If you have any maneuvering room under the clouds, and if you make a good power-off approach, you and your passengers will walk away. To survive this type of accident, you need a lot of luck.

The good news about an engine fire in a multi-engine airplane is that luck is not as big a factor, which is also the bad news. If your skill matches the capabilities of the aircraft, you can continue to a safe landing. But if the skills aren't there, all the luck in the world won't save you.

When the engine quits on a single-engine airplane, the airplane will fly itself. There is no tendency to roll or yaw and the nose will pitch down to maintain the trim setting.

In a twin with an engine failure, the demands of aircraft control are extensive, especially when the airspeed is low and the power on the operating engine is high. When an engine quits in a twin, the airplane will fall out of the sky if you don't maintain control.

Rudder Control

The most important skill during an engine-out emergency is rudder consciousness. When an engine quits in a high-power low-airspeed situation, the airplane yaws and requires rudder pressure. As soon as the attitude indicator shows a roll, you must instinctively react with your feet. If you correct with aileron to stop the roll, the drag induced by the aileron will aggravate the situation.

The pilot who allows the airplane to yaw from side to side in turbulence; who banks the airplane twenty degrees to make a five degree heading change on the localizer; who cannot hold the wing down in a cross-wind landing while steering the airplane with the rudder; and the pilot who always looks at the turn coordinator to determine the quality of a turn is not rudder conscious.

When encountering turbulence in VFR conditions, use the rudder to hold the nose on a point on the horizon. In IFR conditions, use the rudder to make heading corrections of less than five degrees. Take some aerobatic instruction to sharpen your rudder coordination skills. When you can perform nice point rolls, and when you can take-off and land the airplane in a 15 knot cross wind, you'll be rudder conscious.

Maintain Control

The next important skill for handling multi-engine emergencies is the ability to prioritize your thinking and concentrate on the important tasks. When an engine quits, the most important task is to maintain control. Refer to the attitude indicator and use as much rudder and as little aileron as possible to level the wings. Adjust the pitch to near level and then adjust rudder pressure until you can let go of the ailerons without inducing a roll.

At this point, many pilots worry about airspeed. But remember, airspeed depends on pitch. Regardless of how many engines are turning, if the nose is below the horizon, the airspeed will increase and if the nose is above the horizon, it will decrease. During the first seconds after an engine failure, keep the pitch near level flight.

Heading & Airspeed

Heading control is next. For example, if an engine fails during an approach, prompt attention to the heading will allow you to continue the approach. Glance at the heading indicator, determine the direction and amount of correction required and then, using the rudder, bank the airplane slightly in the desired direction.

Now, look at the airspeed to determine if the pitch needs adjustment. I'm certain there are some multi-engine pilots squirming as they read this. What about the boost pumps? What about pushing all the engine controls to the firewall? What about identifying and feathering the dead engine? What about the checklist?

These things come immediately to mind after an engine failure, but none of them are as important as aircraft control. To sacrifice aircraft control for any of them could be fatal. Do nothing else until you have the airplane under control, regardless of how long it takes.

Routine Vs. Procedure

In the second phase of an engine-out emergency, you must follow a routine that puts the aircraft in the best configuration in the fewest possible steps. Notice that I referred to a routine, not a procedure. A procedure is the order in which tasks should be accomplished, and a routine is a procedure that is performed instinctively.

I fly a variety of twins in IFR conditions, from both the right and left seat, so my engine-out routine is generic. It begins with the power levers, and proceeds in a clockwise fashion around the power quadrant. I begin by pushing all the power levers forward, followed by the propeller controls, throttles and mixture controls.

I then move over to the lever at the three o'clock position from the power quadrant. Depending on the airplane, it could be the flap lever or the landing gear lever. If it's the flaps, I raise them. If it's the gear lever, I raise it if I want climb and lower it if I want descend.

On my way around the quadrant, I check the fuel valves and make sure they're in the correct position. Then I move to the boost pumps, which are usually at the nine o'clock position, and turn them on. From there I go to the other gear/flap control and position it as mentioned earlier. Finally, my hand is back at the 12 o'clock position where I rest it on the throttles and make a decision: Do I want to fix or feather?

If time is short, I feather the engine and position the throttle, mixture and propeller controls on the quadrant to match the position of the rudder pedals. I try not to think about left and right, I just position the controls to match my feet. When this is done, the dead engine is feathered. When time allows, I secure the engine and read the checklist.

This doesn't work exactly the same in every airplane. For example, in an Aero Commander, you reach overhead to get the boost pumps. But the concept is always the same; a routine that achieves results with a minimum of subjective reasoning.

Most multi-engine pilots with whom I have flown don't have this type of routine. In an emergency, they expect to do a different thing for each situation. I need a routine that safely achieves the desired configuration with few mental gymnastics. During training, on check rides and during an actual emergency, I've found myself halfway through the routine before my aged and abused brain has caught up.

The best thing about my routine is that I can do it without taking my eyes off the instrument panel. I've practiced it often enough that I can do it in my sleep. I believe this alone makes a safe IFR transition to single-engine flight possible.

The final step in a successful emergency requires that you choose the right alternatives. Don't make an ILS approach at your destination with oneengine if there are higher ceilings, longer runways, or easier approaches somewhere else. Likewise, don't return to your departure airport if other alternatives are better. Once things in the cockpit settle down, you have plenty of time to make the right decisions, so don't rush things.

I have 4000 multi-engine hours, of which 750 hours are in IMC. I won't fly a twin in the clouds unless I have recent VFR experience in the airplane, unless I know where everything is and how it works, and unless I know I can perform my engine failure checklist without fumbling.

I believe that twins are safe for some pilots for those pilots who memorize and practice emergency procedures. If you cannot maintain professional proficiency in a twin, stick with a single.

We'll close this book with a section devoted to a different aspect of aircraft handling...the rollout. In particular, landing on runways made slick by rain.

Hydroplaning

You just descended through a low overcast and brought your airplane safely onto a rainsoaked runway, but before you have time to congratulate yourself, the aircraft skids out of control and ends up in a ditch faster than you can blink an eye. What happened?

Hydroplaning is cited as the cause of more than half of all off-runway accidents. Your pilot technique may be superb, but all that skill won't make a difference if you suddenly take an expensive and embarrassing ride off the runway some night. Hydroplaning can be easily avoided, but it's prevention should begin before the tires contact the pavement.

Of all the types of precipitation that contaminate a runway, rain must be considered equally as dangerous as ice or snow, especially when it occurs on an irregular or poorly drained surface. You are more likely to encounter standing water on a runway than any other hazard at any time of the year.

At low speed (such as taxiing), a tire will displace water that has accumulated on a paved surface. Hydroplaning will occur as speed increases and the tire cannot push this layer of water away from it. The tire breaks contact with the surface and is supported all or in part by the water itself. This causes a partial to total loss of braking and steering control.

Research conducted by the National Aeronautics and Space Administration (NASA) during the 1950s and 1960s found three forms of hydroplaning: dynamic, viscous and reverted rubber.

Dynamic Hydroplaning

Dynamic hydroplaning occurs when a rolling tire contacts a flooded surface and does not displace the fluid fast enough for the tire to make contact with that surface. Hydrodynamic pressure builds underneath the tire, creating an upward force that literally lifts the tire from the surface and causes the tire to stop spinning completely. This complete separation of tire-from-surface is called total dynamic hydroplaning.

The hydroplaning speed can be precisely calculated for any aircraft. The minimum total hydroplaning speed in knots is equal to nine times the square root of the tire pressure in psi. This equation pertains to a rotating tire as it rolls from a dry surface onto a flooded one.

Later research discovered that a non-rotating tire will hydroplane at a slower speed: 7.7 times the square root of tire pressure in psi.

For example, the typical single-engine airplane has a tire pressure of 36 psi. The square root of 36 is 6, times 9 equals 54 knots. The airplane will hydroplane at approximately 54 knots, perhaps during rollout. If the tires are locked during landing, the equation changes to 6 times 7.7 or 46 knots.

The greater the tire pressure, the faster the speed needed to hydroplane. A large jet with a tire pressure of 120 psi will hydroplane at 99 knots.

Conversely, the lower the pressure, the slower the speed needed to hydroplane. This can be quite a problem for light aircraft since hydroplaning speed is often lower than landing speed, almost ensuring some hydroplaning upon landing if water is present. An extreme example is an aircraft with large balloon-like tundra tires. With a tire pressure of four psi, the hydroplaning speed is only 18 knots! (15 knots for a non-rotating tire).

A fairly thick layer of standing water is necessary to support dynamic hydroplaning. Fortunately, on a well-drained runway, this can be difficult to find over large areas of the surface.

Researchers have concluded that it is almost impossible to determine the depth of this layer, since the depth varies depending on the rainfall intensity, runway slope, runway texture and tire tread. A crosswind can also exacerbate the problem by keeping the water near the highest point on the runway, or crown, thereby preventing it from draining.

It has been determined that standing water depths greater than 0.1 inches on an average runway cause full dynamic hydroplaning. Partial dynamic hydroplaning can also occur, usually when only a portion of the tire makes contact with the paved surface. This occurs at a considerably slower speed than total dynamic hydroplaning

Viscous Hydroplaning

Viscous hydroplaning is the most common type of hydroplaning. It occurs at lesser water depths and slower speeds than dynamic hydroplaning.

Viscous hydroplaning occurs when a thin film of water, usually less than a hundreth of an inch, lubricates the paved surface. This is similar to a highway surface in the rain, where the water rises and mixes with oil, fuel and rubber deposits, bringing them to the surface. The friction of the surface is drastically reduced, even at low speed. A dry, clean runway, for example, has a friction coefficient of 0.75 to 0.90. When a coating of water is present, the coefficient can be as low as 0.10.

Both the texture of the pavement and the tire tread affect viscous hydroplaning. In general, the runway must be smooth, in conjunction with a thin tire tread. Water is of lesser importance. You can encounter viscous hydroplaning while taxiing or turning quickly on a wet surface, as when exiting a runway

Reverted Rubber

The third and least understood type of hydroplaning is known as reverted rubber hydroplaning. It occurs when a locked tire skids across a damp or icy runway at a ground speed less than 20 knots and generates enough heat (up to 600° F) to produce steam, which then lifts the tire from the surface.

This steam-generated heat also changes the portion of the tire in contact with the steam back to its original gummy, uncured state. Upon examination, the tire may show signs of this phenomenon with elliptically shaped patches of tacky rubber on its surface.

You may occasionally notice white streaks on some runways. These are areas believed to have been steam-cleaned by the reverted rubber hydroplaning process.

Researchers have found, however, that runway texture does not appear to affect the creation of reverted rubber, since skids occur equally on all runway textures, from coarse to smooth

Other Variables

Some of the variables which can lead to a hydroplaning accident have already been discussed. Understanding the variables that are within your control can help prevent one of these accidents. These variables include: water depth, runway condition, tire condition and pressure, the final approach and landing. Of equal importance are the condition of the brakes and aircraft weight.

As previously mentioned, water depth plays an important role in dynamic hydroplaning. Landing immediately after rain has thoroughly soaked the runway will make you a candidate for this type of hydroplaning.

If possible, delay the landing at least 15 to 20 minutes after a downpour to allow the runway time to drain. Most runways are crowned in the center to prevent standing water from accumulating. Under no-wind conditions, most runways provide adequate drainage. Beware of a crosswind greater than 10 knots though, as water tends to accumulate on the upwind side of the runway.

Grooved Runways

A runway that is grooved and sloped properly to channel water away from it will lower the depth of any standing water. The likelihood of hydroplaning is greatly reduced on a grooved surface when the rainfall rate is less than two inches per hour. A level four storm (which is classified as very strong by the National Weather Service) can produce as much as two inches of rain per hour.

You can determine if a runway is grooved by reviewing the airport information in the *Airport/Facility Directory*. For Jeppesen users, this is indicated on the airport information page under the heading Additional Runway Information.

The texture (coarse or smooth) and any additional contaminates such as ice or compacted snow affect hydroplaning action; a coarse surface provides greater traction and friction, while a smooth one decreases these factors. When possible, ask about runway condition before beginning the approach.

Tire condition and pressure can also contribute to a hydroplaning accident. A tire in poor condition and improperly inflated can send you for an unexpected ride. If the tire tread is greater than the depth of the standing water, hydroplaning should not occur

Techniques to Avoid an Accident

Final approach and landing are areas in which you have greater control. Proper technique during approach and landing can lessen the chances for an accident. Here are a few hints:

• Fly a stabilized approach with a constant rate of descent and avoid excessive speed. Be prepared to go around if runway conditions do not look good.

• Land at the slowest touchdown speed possible. Your speed when crossing the threshold should not exceed 1.3 Vs (corrected for wind).
• At airports with long runways, avoid touching down on the first 2,000 feet. Vulcanization from repeated landings builds up thin sheets of rubber which coat the surface and are slippery when wet.
• Avoid drifting sideways by using crosswind technique to keep the airplane aligned with the runway centerline.
• This is not the time to make a grease it on landing. Make a firm touchdown and try not to bounce.
• Get the nosewheel down quickly; do not hold it off for aerodynamic braking. Lightly apply forward pressure to increase the weight on the nosewheel, but don't over do it. By decreasing the weight on the main tires, you could worsen the situation by causing them to hydroplane. Nosewheel tire pressures are usually lower than that of the main gear tires. This can result in the nosewheel hydroplaning even though the main wheels are not affected.
• Steer with the rudder pedals and do not brake until the aircraft slows below the point where hydroplaning can occur. This should not be a problem on a long runway.
• If a skid occurs, try to align the aircraft centerline with the runway centerline. Do not use braking.

Look Before You Leap

A hydroplaning accident can be avoided by good preflight preparation, which should include details about runway conditions, and proper tire maintenance. Carefully check the condition of the tires, paying particular attention to tire pressure and tread wear. Finally, after this discussion, remember to think twice before rolling into an innocent-looking puddle on the runway. It could be a very expensive and embarrassing ride. It will certainly be one you'll remember forever.

Index